# Overcoming Anxiety

# OVERCOMING ANXIETY

A positive approach to dealing with severe
anxiety in your life

Betty McLellan

ALLEN & UNWIN

*To the memory of my parents*
*Lil and Dave McLellan*

© Betty McLellan 1992
This book is copyright under the Berne Convention.
No reproduction without permission. All rights reserved.

First published 1992
Allen & Unwin Pty Ltd
9 Atchison St, St. Leonards, NSW 2065 Australia

National Library of Australia
Cataloguing-in-Publication entry:

McLellan, Betty.

Overcoming anxiety.

Bibliography.
Includes index.
ISBN 1 86373 078 8.

1. Anxiety—Treatment—Popular works. 2. Women—
Mental health. I. Title.

616.8522068

Set in 11/12.5pt Bembo by Adtype Graphics, North Sydney

Printed by SRM Production Services Sdn Bhd, Malaysia
10 9 8 7 6 5 4 3 2

# Contents

# Preface

IN January 1989, I attended the first Women's Studies Summer Institute at Deakin University which, thanks to the vision and hard work of Robyn Rowland and Renate Klein, proved to be a wonderful experience for the many women who attended from all over Australia and New Zealand.

Dale Spender was the 'Feminist in Residence', and I was fortunate enough to be one of the participants in her course on *The Nature of Knowledge*. One of the points Dale emphasised over and over again throughout the course was the need for women to know what they know. We must ask questions like: What do I know? What do I need to know? How do I know what I know? How does my own feminist construction of knowledge differ from the dominant patriarchal construction? How can I express what I know I know?

Over those two weeks, the conviction grew within me that I had some very important knowledge about the cause and treatment of severe anxiety in women, and it was time I took steps to give that knowledge expression! I reminded myself that, on the question of cause of anxiety, I had studied many different theories and, more importantly, had developed my own theory of cause from a boldly feminist perspective. On the question of treatment, I had found a treatment method that was very effective and had, in fact, proved its effectiveness in my own practice as a psychotherapist.

This book is the expression of what I know is my unique knowledge on this topic.

To Dale Spender—inspirer and encourager of women—I say a special thanks for the inspiration and encouragement you gave to me during the Summer Institute and since that time.

To Coralie McLean and Jan Woodley—strong, witty, courageous feminists, my true friends over many years—thank you for your reading and re-reading of the manuscript, your gentle criticisms, helpful suggestions, and above all, your enthusiastic support.

To Shelley Dempsey, Jenny Binnie, Gina Mercer, Coralie McLean, Jan Woodley, Madge Sceriha, Pauline Woodbridge, Sheryl Cornack, Baillie Carleton, Bronwyn Patton, Peta Picton, Ginni Hall and Jenny Stone—my sincere thanks for your willingness to share your personal stories of powerlessness, invisibility and emotional deprivation. To all of you I am deeply grateful.

# The book and how to use it

ANXIETY is something all women are familiar with. As girls, teenagers, newly-weds, wives, mothers, single women, divorced women, lesbians, factory workers, office workers, professional women, whatever lifestyle we choose, it is never difficult for us to find something to worry about, something to feel anxious about. How many of us have been accused of actually creating things to worry about? 'If there's nothing to worry about, you'll make something up, just so you won't be disappointed!' we are told; or, 'You're never happy unless you're worrying about something!'

## Normal anxiety

While it is true to say that some women have a tendency to feel *more* anxious about *more* things than other women, it is also true that every woman knows what it feels like to be anxious. All of us have experienced anxiety before an exam, a job interview, or making a speech. Most of us experienced anxiety about having sex for the first time. Most women experience anxiety, to a greater or lesser degree, about what people think of them. I wonder what they thought of me. I wonder how I came across. Maybe I should have smiled more. Maybe I should have smiled less. I wonder why people never seem to take me seriously.

1

Maybe I should be more assertive. But if I'm too assertive, people mightn't like me. These kinds of anxious thoughts are not uncommon for many women on a daily basis.

For women who choose to be married, there is an underlying (almost unconscious) anxiety about marriage itself, about the requirement to give up your own individual identity and become part of your husband's life; about whether the man of your dreams who seems so wonderful now, who speaks of equality, respect, sharing, of a partnership that will be 'different', will be changed by the power and status marriage gives to men. Also when you are married or living in a long-term relationship with a man, there is often anxiety about what your partner is thinking, why he chooses not to talk much, why he chooses not to share his innermost thoughts with you any more. There is the anxiety caused by blaming yourself. 'What am I doing wrong? If only I could find the key to open him up, so that we could both be happy again.' Blaming ourselves for something that is not our fault produces incredible anxiety because we commit all our energy to a task that is literally impossible. If someone chooses not to open up, there is absolutely nothing we can do about it.

Then, there is the added anxiety caused by the realisation that your partnership is not going to be any different from all the others where a woman is largely taken for granted, necessary to keep the man's life comfortable but not important enough to talk to, or listen to, or treat with the kind of respect accorded to his male friends.

Also, for many women in relationships with men, there is a continuing anxiety about the possibility of becoming pregnant, the nagging concern, however slight, that this could be the time your contraceptive does not work. For other women who dearly want to be pregnant, there is anxiety about not becoming pregnant.

For mothers, there is a built-in anxiety about your children's welfare. Are they eating the kind of food that will nourish and sustain them and allow them to grow up to be healthy, happy adults? How are they managing at school? Do they have friends among their peers? Do they relate well to adults? How are they handling the normal disappointments and frustrations of life? Do

I listen to them and empathise when they want to talk about their unhappiness? Do I give them enough praise so that they learn to appreciate their own achievements and feel good about themselves? All of these thoughts plus the daily routine of having to remember each child's schedule and get them to school, ballet lessons, tennis coaching, swimming lessons, football practice, etc., etc. on time, mean that a lot of anxious energy is used up in the role of mother.

When children become teenagers there are different things to worry about, like where they are, who they are with, what they are doing, how to handle their rebelliousness, how much freedom to give them, and how much discipline is good for them. On top of all that, there is the overriding anxiety about whether or not you are preparing them properly to take their place in the adult world and be happy with who they are.

Not all women choose marriage and family. There are some who choose to remain single all their lives, some who choose to become single again after having been married, and some who choose to live in lesbian relationships. Many of these women are also mothers striving to bring up their children in the best possible way, and are therefore subject to all the same stresses and strains associated with mothering.

Another source of anxiety for single, divorced or lesbian women, is the need to contend with the derogatory attitude that exists toward them in a society that invests a lot of energy in keeping women in their proper place. This patriarchal society, so desperately intent on guarding male power and making sure women have no access to the power structures of the society in anything but a token way, works hard at making marriage and family appear to be the only real alternative for women, the only path that will make women truly happy. Regardless of the studies that show clearly that married women on the whole are less happy than single women, the patriarchy continues to point women in the direction of marriage, and to punish them in subtle and not-so-subtle ways if they choose otherwise. So, we see that no matter what a woman chooses to do with her life, anxiety is a very familiar experience.

Anxiety about health is another area of concern—anxiety

about the health of one's partner, children, grandchildren, aging parents, as well as anxiety about one's own health.

Added to all this, there is anxiety about the kind of global issues that threaten the very existence of the human race: the destruction of the earth through nuclear warfare, the increasing pollution of the environment, the hole in the ozone layer, the greenhouse effect, and so on.

Believe it or not, all of the anxieties mentioned so far come under the heading of 'normal anxiety'. In all situations that are worrying or stressful, anxiety is the normal response. Indeed, if you are preparing for an important job interview, or if your teenager fails to come home at all one night, it would *not* be normal if you were not anxious. Anxiety is a normal response in situations like those discussed above.

## Abnormal anxiety

There is, however, another kind of anxiety which could be said to be abnormal, and it is that abnormal anxiety that is the subject of this book. *How do you know if the anxiety you are feeling is normal or abnormal?* It is actually fairly simple to discern. There are two criteria. First, normal anxiety is said to be *specific*, that is, it is related to a specific event. I am about to have a job interview and am feeling anxious. The job interview is the specific event that is causing my anxiety, therefore my anxiety is normal. Second, normal anxiety *has a limited life*, in that, when the event is over, so is the anxiety. Even if the event about which a person is anxious results in failure, the anxiety still usually disappears. Even if I said all the wrong things in the interview and ruined my chances of getting the job, my anxiety would still disappear. In such situations, it would be replaced by another emotion, such as disappointment, or anger, or relief, but the anxiety itself is over.

The focus of this book is on women who experience the kind of anxiety that is *non-specific* and that *does not have a limited life*. This kind of severe anxiety can be there from the moment a woman wakes up in the morning till she finally gets to sleep at night, with no obvious explanation. It is not related to any

4

specific event. The confusing thing is that it often does *appear* to be attached to something specific—for example, when an anxiety-sufferer fears she is going to have a heart attack, or is convinced she has a brain tumour, or fears she may do something terrible to her children—but, in fact, the anxiety is not about anything real. It is anticipatory anxiety, anxiety about what *might* happen, and it takes over a person's whole being and renders her helpless. Most women who experience this kind of severe anxiety feel totally at the mercy of the anxiety that grips them. It is as if they no longer have control over their own lives. A more detailed description of the condition can be found in chapter one.

## Why a self-help book for women?

This book focuses on severe anxiety as it is experienced by women because, in my practice as a psychotherapist, more and more of my clients are women suffering from severe anxiety conditions, panic attacks and agoraphobia. The emphasis is on self-help so that anxiety-sufferers, their families and friends, their doctors and therapists can gain a better understanding of this hitherto baffling condition and learn successful ways of treating it. Due to the appalling lack of information available, most people still do not know that this is a condition that *can* be cured, provided the guidelines for treatment are followed carefully.

Another reason for writing this book is that education about the condition is one important step in the process towards cure. Given that severe anxiety causes a woman to feel unable to control what she knows is irrational fear and panic, an important treatment requirement is that the anxiety-sufferer learn all she can about the condition so that she begins to experience a degree of control. Ignorance about anything leaves one feeling vulnerable, but education or knowledge brings with it a sense of control.

Realising the importance of giving my clients something to read to supplement the teaching I have tried to do as part of the initial therapy sessions, I have spent years searching for something down-to-earth, readable, intelligent, and accurate in terms of the kind of treatment strategies I know work, but have found nothing in medical, psychological, or popular literature that satisfies me fully. There is one source which has been helpful in terms of setting out effective ways of treating the condition on a day-to-day basis (Weekes 1962), but nothing which also attempts to discuss what causes it in the first place. My experience as a therapist is that almost everyone who comes with this problem asks me: Why? Why has this happened to me? How did it start? What caused it? Where did I go wrong? Because these questions are being asked, they cannot be ignored. Therefore, a reasonably comprehensive discussion of cause must be included in any book on treatment.

## Who is this book for?

This book is primarily for women who experience severe anxiety, panic attacks, vague but persistent anxiety, and/or agoraphobia. While it may be true that the best thing an anxiety-sufferer can do is see a therapist who knows something about anxiety conditions, there are two things that often prevent that happening. One is that it has been fairly difficult in the past to find a therapist who feels confident about the effective treatment of severe anxiety; and the other is that the very nature of the condition causes women to want to avoid social contacts of any kind, and face-to-face contact with a therapist is one of those social situations that are avoided.

Women with this condition tend to narrow their social contacts right down to a bare minimum. Those whose main activity is working in the home and taking care of their children, tend to become more and more isolated in the home, avoiding going out as much as possible. Those who are in paid employment tend to go to work, struggle through the day, and come home from work, avoiding all social contacts other than those absolutely necessary to sustain them in their jobs. For many women, then, going to a therapist is not even considered as an option.

Recently I was invited by our local television station to appear on an afternoon program aimed primarily at women, to talk about a public seminar I was about to present on anxiety. Following that interview, I received many phonecalls from women suffering from anxiety, wanting to talk about their situation over the phone, wanting information, asking me to recommend something they could read to help them deal with their anxiety. I gave them as much time on the phone as I could, told them about Claire Weekes' book, *Self Help for your Nerves*, and urged them to come to the seminar. On the day of the public seminar, I was disappointed but not surprised when only twelve women attended. This condition, by its very nature, often prevents women going out to get help. My hope is that this book, aimed at enabling anxiety-sufferers to help themselves, will be the beginning of recovery for many women who have, till now, felt that their lives were slipping out of their own control.

It should be mentioned here that there will be some anxiety-sufferers—only a relatively small number—who may not benefit from reading this book. They are the people whose anxiety is complicated by other problems, such as serious mental illness, chronic depression, and/or a problem-relationship that needs to keep the anxiety alive in order to give the relationship a reason for continuing (see chapter 6).

The book is also written for family members and friends of anxiety-sufferers who care about them and want to be able to give them the right kind of support.

It is also for therapists, psychiatrists, doctors, and other health workers, many of whom (like myself, for many years) have been stumbling around in the dark in relation to severe and persistent anxiety conditions. Until now, there has been very little available for them to read which would encourage them to have any real confidence in a particular treatment method.

Men who suffer from severe anxiety will find this book helpful too. I have no doubt that the main criticism of this book will be that I have focused solely on women. 'Men suffer from anxiety too', they will say, 'so why exclude men?' I want to say very clearly that my intention here is not to exclude men, but rather to focus on women. In every area of life, from the earliest

7

years we can remember right up to the present day, girls and women have had to adapt what they have heard and read to make it apply to themselves. Most research and writing in psychology, sociology and anthropology presents human life and behaviour from a male perspective. Most theological and philosophical literature is written about God and men in deliberately male terms. Most movies invite the audience to view the characters and the plot from a male perspective. What I am doing here is simply choosing to write about severe anxiety conditions as they affect women, and inviting men to adapt what they read to apply to their own situation. I believe the causes of severe anxiety in men are somewhat different from the causes for women, but the method of treatment is the same, and men will find the treatment section immediately helpful.

Feminists, also, will find this book interesting and helpful. Those reading with an open mind will appreciate its value as a practical, down-to-earth application of feminist philosophy, a reminder, on the one hand, of the on-going devastating effects of the patriarchy's attitude toward and treatment of women and, on the other hand, of the necessity for us to continue to work for the empowerment of women.

## Organisation of the book

The organisation of the book you are about to read is simple. In the first chapter, there is a fairly detailed description of this anxiety condition that renders so many women helpless. Over and over again I am told by women in therapy: 'You don't know what it's like. Only someone who has experienced this kind of anxiety and these kinds of panic attacks, really knows what it's like.' My own experience of it is not first-hand. Rather, my experience has come through empathising with women as they attempt to tell me what it feels like. I must say that even this 'second-hand' experience is sometimes so shattering as to be almost more than I can bear, so to experience it first-hand must be absolutely devastating. In my description of the condition in chapter 1, then, I attempt to bring together what clinicians say about it and what anxiety-sufferers themselves say when they try to describe how it feels.

Chapter 2 is important because it looks at the place assigned to women in this blatantly male-centred, male-controlled society, and suggests that anxiety in women is a direct result of powerlessness and absence of control at every level. I argue that the age in which we live at this present time in history is for women 'the age of anxiety', and that in order to prevent the escalation of serious anxiety problems amongst women, we need to open our eyes and see and understand the mechanisms that operate in society to keep all women in a powerless state, be outraged by what we see, and express that outrage until change is effected. There is no doubt in my mind that the total lack of control a woman feels at a personal level when she is in the grip of an anxiety attack is a psychological and emotional manifestation of the lack of control she feels as a woman in a society made by men, for men. Much of the time, she is powerless; she is invisible; and she is emotionally deprived.

The question that arises, of course, is: If severe anxiety conditions in women are related to absence of control over their own lives, how come *all* women in our society do not develop such anxiety? This very important question is addressed in the following chapters on cause.

Chapters 3, 4, and 5 all deal with the question: What causes severe anxiety and panic conditions in individual women? There are two things we know for certain about cause. The first is that there is no one simple cause that applies to everybody, and the second is that the cause of each woman's anxiety is to be found within that individual woman. The anxiety-sufferer must engage in her own individual enquiry about possible causes of her own condition. In other words, she must take control of her own healing.

The way I have chosen to deal with the question of cause is to outline the three theories from psychological literature that I believe present most clearly what I see happening in the lives of my clients. These are psychoanalytic, existential, and feminist theories. Within the framework of each of these theories, I have chosen to highlight three experiences women commonly talk

9

about as causing them serious distress: powerlessness, invisibility and emotional deprivation. Deliberate focus is placed on the issue of 'powerlessness' as it is discussed in psychoanalytic theory, 'invisibility' as it relates to existential theory, and 'emotional deprivation' as it is revealed in feminist theory. The discussion of the theories proceeds in such a way that a woman suffering from anxiety can begin to try the theories on, and develop her own theory about the cause of her own condition. If you are an anxiety-sufferer, you will find that some of the theories you read about in these chapters do not fit with your experience at all, while others will feel just right. Taking control of your own healing includes a desire to understand your own condition and develop some kind of theory about how it all started.

Each of the chapters dealing with cause seeks to present a different perspective on the cause of anxiety-conditions in women. Although there are obvious similarities among the theories, and sometimes those similarities are pointed out, there is no real attempt in this book to connect them with each other. Each theory is intended to stand on its own, and is presented for the purpose of allowing an anxiety-sufferer to test it against her own experience in the hope that some light will be shed on the puzzle about how her own anxiety might have originated.

In the final chapter, I outline the kind of treatment I have used with great success over the last few years. Underlying all that I say about treatment is the very strong advice: 'Stop trying to control your anxiety, and begin to develop a real determination to be in control of your own *healing*.' How to do that is outlined step-by-step in chapter 6.

Again, there is no direct connection between the chapters dealing with cause and the final chapter. The strength of Morita treatment is that it stands on its own. Cure through Morita treatment does not depend on any understanding of cause. For that reason, I strongly advise anxiety-sufferers who are looking for immediate relief from their anxiety, to read chapters 1 and 6 *first*, because they will speak to you immediately. Only when you feel ready should you go back and read the chapters about cause.

Those women who make the decision to bring about their own healing, with or without the help of a therapist, and who follow the guidelines set out in this book, will no longer feel like women who have lost control. Rather, by giving up the desperate need to control your anxiety, you will gain a sense of control over your own destiny that you never thought possible.

# 1

# Description of severe anxiety

PAULA, 28, mother of two, was standing in line at the supermarket with two people ahead of her and three behind her. For no apparent reason she began to feel nervous. What was wrong with her? She had been there a hundred times before, and today was no different from all the other times. She told herself she was just being silly, but the nervousness grew and grew until she was experiencing real panic. What could she do? She felt trapped. Unable to go forward and unable to go back, she knew there was no way to get out of the line without causing a fuss. It was important to her not to draw attention to herself because people would ask her what was wrong, and the truth was she had no idea!

Jane, 45, professional woman, mother of three grown-up children, was driving to work one day along the same route she had driven for more than five years. Waiting in her car at a busy intersection for the traffic light to turn green, she felt suddenly out of control. Her heart was racing. She thought she might be having a heart attack. What could she do? She wanted to get out of the car and run, but managed to wait till the light turned green and pulled her car over to the side of the road. Her breathing became faster. She began hyperventilating. She was in the grip of panic. If it was not a heart attack, what was it? She had absolutely no idea what was happening to her.

Tracey, 19, had been unemployed for 18 months before getting a job as a housemaid at a large motel. It was not the kind of job she had hoped for but it was better than nothing. She had been there about six months and felt a sense of satisfaction when she heard positive comments about her work. The bosses seemed happy with her performance and the other workers seemed to like her, too. One day as she walked into one of the motel units to start the usual routine of stripping the beds, cleaning the bathroom, vacuuming the floor, she became aware of a slight headache. Also, she noticed the palms of her hands were sweating and her legs felt quite shaky. She felt strangely light-headed as if she was going to faint. What was happening to her? She could not remember ever feeling so frightened before, but she knew there was absolutely nothing to be frightened about.

## The first attack

This is how anxiety starts for many people. They are in the middle of an otherwise normal day, doing the same routine things they have done every day for years, when all of a sudden they are overwhelmed with panic. Their first impulse usually is to run away, to get away from the situation they think must be causing it. Their second response, after the worst of it is over and they have regained some of their composure, is to try desperately to figure out what caused the panic. Experience tells them there has to be a cause for everything. Common sense tells them no-one experiences such intense feelings without provocation. There must be a reason.

Their third response, then, after unsuccessfully searching for reasons outside themselves, is to look inside and blame themselves. 'I'm just being silly.' 'I've got to pull myself together.' 'I've got to get a grip on myself.' To blame oneself, however, is never totally satisfying, and the search for an explanation continues. The fact that it defies explanation is the thing that makes it very frightening because, without an explanation, there appears to be no chance of controlling it.

If a connection could be found between a person's panic and the fact that she was about to make a speech, for example, she could simply decide never to make speeches again; or if a connection could be found between her panic and overtiredness, she could decide to be very careful not to become overtired again. When the cause of panic is known, all one has to do to eliminate the possibility of its happening again is get rid of the cause. The fact that the kind of anxiety and panic being addressed here does not actually have an obvious cause makes it impossible to control, and it is for that reason that most anxiety-sufferers feel totally powerless in the face of this mysterious 'thing' that has taken over their lives.

The fourth response (after wanting to run away, then trying to figure out what caused the panic, and then blaming themselves for being 'so silly') is a determination to control the anxiety and ensure that they never experience such panic again. As we will see in later chapters, this determination to control that which cannot be controlled is the most damaging of all the responses, because it sets in place an attitude of mind and a way of living which keeps one's anxiety alive by keeping it in the forefront of one's mind and giving it the kind of attention it ought not have. From the moment the first panic attack subsides, a person carries with her an intense fear that the panic she experienced that day will come again. It is always on her mind, but she finds that the more attention she gives to it, the worse it becomes, and the more she tries to control it, the more it dominates her life.

While the majority of anxiety-sufferers speak of their first anxiety attack as something which came upon them with absolutely no warning, there are others who say in hindsight that they had been experiencing vague, unexplained anxiety feelings for months or years prior to their first severe attack but felt they had always been able to 'control' it.

Still others speak of unexplained physical symptoms over a long period of time—like pains in the chest, difficulty with breathing, headaches and so on—symptoms which prompted numerous visits to the doctor and, in some cases, numerous visits to numerous doctors.

### Stop fighting it

No two people experience anxiety in exactly the same way. It is important, therefore, that anxiety-sufferers find books or magazine articles they can identify with and use that information to explore their own particular experience of anxiety, because knowledge and understanding are crucial. The more a person knows, the stronger she will feel. If you are an anxiety-sufferer, you are much more likely to achieve a cure if you are prepared to stop fighting against your anxiety and address yourself first to trying to understand it, and second to following the steps set out in chapter 6. In other words, if you *decide* to get on top of it, then with the help of this book, you will. It must be said, though, that there is no such thing as an easy option and whoever expects to find one will be disappointed.

'I'll just go to the doctor and get some anti-anxiety pills', some people say. 'Maybe I'll just go and get hypnotised', others say. The easy options do not work. Drugs may make you feel better in the short term, but when the effect of the drugs wears off, the anxiety will be just as bad as ever. Hypnotism may help you learn better ways of relaxing, but will not provide a magic cure for your anxiety.

A cure requires a fair amount of work, but it is not impossible work by any means. It involves getting yourself into a frame of mind which allows you to accept your anxiety as it is; being prepared to read whatever is available to improve your knowledge of the condition; and determining to be in charge of your own life again rather than allowing your fear of another attack to dominate everything you think and say and do. These are not impossible things, but they do require a willingness to work at changing your attitude to yourself as well as your attitude to your anxiety condition.

### Seek to understand the condition

Any attempt at a description of severe anxiety must begin with the experiences of anxiety-sufferers themselves because they are the only ones who can describe the condition from the 'inside'. For this purpose I asked three women if they would be prepared to answer questions about their own experiences of anxiety, which they were only too willing to do. I chose women whose anxiety is mostly behind them and who no longer live in fear of its return. They have learned what to do whenever they experience a hint of anxiety, and consequently live with the certainty that it will never again dominate their lives.

After we hear from these women, we will then look at the way this condition is described in psychological and medical literature, because that source also offers important insights, albeit of a different kind.

## Descriptions from the inside: anxiety-sufferers describe their experiences

The questionnaire sent out to the three women was prepared for the purpose of gaining first-hand descriptions of the experience of severe anxiety. The following is an exact reporting of the questions sent and the answers received from the respondents, with comment from me where appropriate.

*Question 1: How old were you when you had your first anxiety attack?*

Kate: 27 (almost).

Mandy: About 18, I think. First year of University.

Bev: 39 years.

*Question 2: Describe your first attack*

Kate: For some weeks prior to this first 'attack', I had been feeling light-headed and a little dizzy at times. I had seen a GP, who asked whether I was under stress (I said 'No') and decided that I was probably not eating properly. (I certainly was—I was in my health-food phase.)

Then, late one afternoon, while I was at work, I just felt very anxious, tense. I felt shaky. My breathing was fast and shallow; my stomach was tight and knotted; my tongue felt stiff and strange in my mouth. It was very uncomfortable and I just wanted it to go away. I wasn't frightened . . . somehow I knew what it was . . . the feelings were recognisable, but it was extremely unpleasant. This lasted for several hours and then eased. Several days later, it returned.

Mandy: I was walking across a crowded cafeteria at Queensland University carrying a cup of coffee and suddenly

16

my hands shook so much I had to put the cup and saucer down. To this day, I dread having to carry a cup in a saucer and avoid it when possible, though I seem to manage alright when I am forced to do it.

Bev: I woke up about 3 am in a distressed state (as if from a bad dream) very frightened and feeling as if I were choking. I was panicking for air and had to get out of bed and stand at the window and slowly get my breathing going again and settle myself. My heart was beating very loud and fast. There seemed no reason for this state.

Most anxiety-sufferers say the first anxiety attack is the worst because it is so sudden and unexpected, like nothing they have ever experienced before. Kate's experience, though, seems to have come on more slowly than is usually the case, and she even questions whether her first experience could correctly be called an 'attack'. Mandy, too, in response to a later question, indicates that her first attack was not her worst. In answer to question 6, she states that her 'attacks became worse' over the first three years. Leaving aside the question of intensity, then, it is true to say that each anxiety-sufferer experiences her first attack in her own particular way, and while the symptoms (or, the way the anxiety expresses itself) are often quite different, the feeling of not being able to control what is happening is always the same.

*Question 3: How did you feel immediately afterwards?*

Kate: . . . Relieved that I was 'back to normal'
. . . terrified that it might happen again
. . . puzzled as to why this should happen and what had caused it
. . . ashamed that I should be so weak.

Mandy: I felt shaken and surprised, wondering why my body had betrayed me.

Bev: Terrified. Really scared—but didn't know what I was scared of. Distressed and very confused/isolated/lost.

*Question 4: How did you explain the experience to yourself? What did you think was happening? What did you think caused it?*

17

Kate: I decided that something that I couldn't identify was causing me stress—my work, my social isolation, my separation from family and familiar environment (my partner and I had recently moved away).

Although it was not an explanation that entirely satisfied me, I decided that it was a combination of these things that was responsible for the way I felt. However, I kept searching my mind for a more fitting explanation, and I furtively searched out books and articles in libraries and bookshops.

Mandy: I felt self-conscious as an ugly, pimply, chubby, red-headed, freckled teenager, and didn't want people looking at me. Walking across a crowded room, I still didn't want people looking when I was eighteen or so! I put it down to this.

Bev: At first I thought it was an asthma attack—but it wasn't. I then thought it was a reaction to stress and that I was not coping and was having a breakdown. Felt really weak and inadequate because I couldn't manage my emotions. I knew it was related to the stress I was experiencing.

When something traumatic happens in a person's life, a normal response is to try to figure out what caused it. When a cause is not obvious as is always the case with severe anxiety, the tendency is to blame it on something like stress or low self-esteem. Both Kate and Bev blamed stress, while Mandy blamed her low self-esteem. Such diagnoses are often supported by doctors, therapists, family members and friends, but even after the anxiety-sufferer works hard at reducing her stress or raising her self-esteem, she finds that despite all her hard work, the anxiety is still there. Attempting to find an explanation is very important, but the almost total lack of accurate information about the condition in the past (from health professionals, or in the form of accessible reading materials) has made it impossible for people to gain any understanding about what was happening to them.

*Question 5: What did you do to try to 'control' it at that time?*

Kate: The first time . . . nothing. I just hoped it would go away. As the sensations returned every few days and then,

every day, I tried a range of things: I tried to exert sheer
will-power to stave off the onset of these symptoms (and felt
weak and miserable when this failed)—I tried to occupy
myself constantly—I tried desperately to ignore the
symptoms and act as if they were not there.

Mandy: Avoid situations where my hands would shake in
public. Eating soup, smoking, eating, drinking, writing. All
that went on for years.

Bev: Rested—stayed in bed but found that I was really
depressed. Cried a lot. Tried to work out how to change my
life to avoid feeling so bad. Went to counselling on a weekly
basis.

*Question 6: After your first anxiety attack, did your life
change in any way? If so, describe how your life was
different.*

Kate: Life became restricted. My preoccupation was with
myself. The world shrank and was removed from me. There
was no joy in living. However, the physical routines of life
remained the same.

Mandy: Attacks became worse. One day in Canberra three
years later, I could barely force myself to walk across Garema
Place because my whole body was so stiff and trembling.
Had to scurry to a wall. Also, could hardly sign my name on
bank forms.

Bev: I withdrew more and more from any situation that I
thought would cause me stress. Left a relationship . . .
changed my job to one I thought would be less stressful. I
lost confidence in my abilities and in my personality. Became
very 'lost', as I didn't seem able to cope with life as I had
before and as others still seemed able to do.

All three respondents have indicated that their lives changed
fairly dramatically after the onset of anxiety. They refer to a
scaling down of their range of experiences in an attempt to
reduce their anxiety. In her answer to question 5, Mandy said she
would 'avoid situations where (her) hands would shake in
public', and then she listed activities that she no longer felt
comfortable doing. Kate said the same kind of thing in answer to
question 6. 'Life became restricted', she said, and 'the world

shrank'. Bev said she 'withdrew more and more . . . left a relationship . . . changed my job'.

Kate also made reference to something which is always a feature of this condition, and that is, an overwhelming preoccupation with the self. Severe anxiety is such a devastating and puzzling experience that one's mind becomes obsessed with thoughts of it, and therefore of oneself, every waking moment.

Such self-preoccupation also includes hypochondria which, for many anxiety-sufferers, is the most distressing of all the symptoms of the condition. Some attest to the fact that no matter what illness they hear about, it is more than likely they will become obsessed with thoughts of that illness till they go to a doctor and have their fears allayed. Even then, they often need to make several visits to a doctor before their anxiety about that illness subsides.

For anxiety-sufferers who are mothers, self-preoccupation often extends to include preoccupation with the well-being of their children. While it is normal for any mother to experience anxiety in relation to her children's vulnerability, defencelessness and total dependence, especially in the early years, the difference for some anxiety-sufferers is that they become obsessed with thoughts and fears about how their actions might bring harm to their children.

*Question 7: How long did you suffer/have you suffered from this condition?*

Kate: Six months, although the symptoms returned (and will return) periodically after this time—with lessening frequency and intensity.

Mandy: About ten years, although manageable now.

Bev: Five years.

*Question 8: Looking back over the period from your first attack till now, how would you describe the emotional symptoms you have experienced?*

Kate: I felt depressed, cut off from the world, constantly terrified. At times, I feared I was going insane. I felt I had lost touch with myself and was no longer in control of my life. I lost hope.

Mandy: I was extremely nervous most of the time. Always waiting for, and dreading, the next attack of the 'shakes'.

Bev: Shattering! The anxiety attacks seemed to strip away from me confidence that I could cope with life. I often felt I would not survive and had no idea what to do about it. Strategies that had worked well in the past seemed to worsen things. Emotionally I felt disconnected from reality and falling behind the rest of the world . . . Very, very lost and scared, and not knowing how to fix it!

*Question 9: What physical symptoms have you experienced?*

Kate: Light-headedness, over-breathing, hypochondria, knotted stomach, increased heart-beat, trembling, stiff tongue and tight throat, repetitious thoughts.

(At one stage, if I read of a symptom, my body would reproduce it.)

Mandy: I still suffer fatigue easily, as my nerves have frayed over the years I think. My head sometimes feels so full, it would burst. Shaking is the main symptom, also gastritis I had at one time. (I get it rarely now, only under stress—interviews, 'first dates', etc.)

Bev: I had extensive muscular pain in back/shoulders/neck. Physically held myself tight/protected/withdrawn. Constant headaches. Chronically tired.

*Question 10: What is the status of your anxiety condition now? If you have overcome it (mostly or totally), what methods did you use?*

Kate: Ten years later, my condition no longer exerts much control over my life and the symptoms rarely reappear. If they do, the duration is brief. The condition gradually receded when, by accident, worn out and overwhelmed by constantly preparing for battle with my anxiety, I discovered that to give in, accept the symptoms and attach little importance to them in fact lessened their severity. (Very different from *concentrating* on ignoring them.)

Once the condition lost its power to inspire dread, it was overcome.

Mandy: I read books—Ainslie Meares, anything on panic attacks, nerves (Claire Weekes), books on relaxation therapy.

I also became physically fit—shoring the body up against such attacks. I took up moderate running, swimming, dancing, aerobics etc. to ward off attacks. I ate healthier food—an overload of sugar made me feel nervy. I never let my blood sugar get low—I eat every three or four hours or so. I try to get plenty of sleep. I don't sleep all that well still, waking up two or three times a night generally. But I can now drift off again usually, by thinking comforting thoughts to make me feel safe.

I tried meditation informally and sometimes still do it but not often. I listen to 'ambient music' or watch videos to relax. I used to drink a lot—I drink heavily rarely now. I saw psychologists twice. Neither appeared to know what was wrong with me—I didn't know myself.

Now, I look at myself from inside out, not from outside in. I have developed a personal philosophy of sorts which keeps me calm, and I indulge in 'self-talk' when the going gets tough.

Bev: I haven't had an attack since August/September 1989. I have learnt to ward off attacks by learning about the condition and assuring myself there is nothing to fear. This stops acceleration of adrenalin and panic. I had counselling and attended a lecture on anxiety attacks. I try to take responsibility *only* for myself and not expect life to follow old and/or unrealistic expectations. I have changed my expectations to fit what actually is possible for me to have/achieve and am feeling good about that, because I am doing what I want for myself.

I assure myself constantly about achievements I make and how well I cope with day to day issues (some of these have been big issues, i.e. new career moves, purchasing a home, moving interstate).

I am now addressing health problems which are a result (to a great extent) of this condition and stress. I feel I have mostly overcome the attacks and now need to look after myself physically, emotionally and mentally. I now feel strong enough to do this as I don't need to fear further attacks.

When visits to doctors, psychiatrists, therapists, naturopaths, herbalists etc. prove unsuccessful and disappointing, many anxiety-sufferers in desperation develop their own way of dealing with their condition, with varying degrees of success. When Kate discovered 'by accident' that 'to give in, accept the symptoms and attach little importance to them in fact lessened their severity', she actually stumbled on the crucial first step of the method proposed in chapter 6 of this book: a method that has had remarkable success wherever it has been used. Bev discovered the value of 'learning about the condition and assuring myself there is nothing to fear'.

The method developed by Mandy is also an important one. Concentrating on physical fitness, lowering alcohol intake, indulging in self-talk to keep oneself calm, thinking positive thoughts, are all very necessary activities for anxiety-sufferers. It must be said, however, that while this method alone may sometimes lead to a cure, there are other times when it will merely help a person live with her anxiety a little more comfortably. This prompts the question: What factor causes this method sometimes to effect a cure and sometimes not? The answer is found in Kate's parenthetical remark that to accept one's symptoms and attach little importance to them is 'very different from *concentrating* on ignoring them'.

If one's attempts at physical exercise, healthy eating, good sleep patterns, relaxation, meditation, and so on, are always combined with the thought: 'I am doing this for the purpose of getting rid of my anxiety', then the anxiety will remain. It is the actual *focusing* on the symptoms for whatever reason—even for the purpose of getting rid of them or ignoring them—that causes them to persist. So, if physical exercise, healthy eating, etc. is the method chosen to deal with anxiety, it is imperative that those activities are done for their own sake. In other words, physical exercise must be embarked upon for no other reason than that one wants to do physical exercise and become physically fit. One's concentration must be on the physical exercise for its own sake.

When an anxiety-sufferer becomes lost in thoughts of the physical exercise she is involved in, even just for one hour, she looks back and sees that for that one hour, she was free of anxiety symptoms. The more a person can manage to move her focus away from her anxiety, the more relief she will get. This, of course, is no easy feat, but involvement in physical exercise is often a good place to start.

If you are swimming, for example, it is important to try to move your attention away from how you are feeling and on to what your body is doing. Observe the details of the physical activity—how your arm comes over, the way your hand cuts into the water, what your feet are doing. Allow yourself to be absorbed by those thoughts. At first, you will still find yourself sneaking a thought about how you are feeling, whether your anxiety is less than it was ten minutes ago and so on, but if you persevere you will find that every day it becomes easier to concentrate on the activity itself, and you are more and more able to allow your anxiety to fade into the background. There will be much more on this method of treatment later.

As well as answering all the questions in the questionnaire, two of the respondents sent additional (very personal) material, in the hope that readers would find it helpful. The following is the full, unedited text received from both women.

Kate included with her questionnaire several pages of excerpts from the writing she did during the height of her anxiety some years ago. This is a deeply personal account of the pain and anguish suffered by someone overwhelmed by the uncontrollable nature of her condition.

### 5th May

... (Not long ago) I felt at one with my surroundings—a part of the world.

But only one month after I commenced my (new) job ... I began experiencing some distressing sensations. These have persisted. I have referred to them as depression but in fact I am not depressed, or not primarily so, but rather I am suffering some sort of anxiety state which removes me from the world and locks me in my own stomach, which is tense and knotted. My tongue is stiff and will not wind itself fluently around words and my whole body is tight and waiting to face some crisis which does not materialise. My heart beats and I breathe fast, but there is no cause for these bodily reactions. These sensations come and go (but remain in some

24

form fairly constantly). At their worst, I fear I am going insane and will reach a point where I can no longer cope with them, but will start screaming uncontrollably. At calmer times, I tell myself I am strong and will handle this. I have tried to analyse this experience and can only pose possibilities, any of which may explain what's happening or then again may not.

I think perhaps I worked at such fever pitch (in my last job) that my body is using this outlet now; or perhaps I am anxious at the loss of my status, my friends, my family, my place in the order of things; perhaps there is some physical basis (unlikely); or then maybe I am reacting to my very distressing and depressing job; or it could be that I am subconsciously anxious that I am adrift in the world; or perhaps . . . perhaps I can continue to postulate ad nauseum.

Whatever the cause, it seems the reaction is beyond my conscious control and I cannot just will it away. It does affect my state of mind and I often feel different, separate from others and shut off from the world around me. Time hangs heavily and the whole world appears a small, bitter and brutal place.

I would guess that a way out is to develop some interests, some relationships, and continue the search for a meaning in life! That's all!!

My mental state is reflected in my physical well-being. While I am quite well, as usual, I get a little obsessed with my health (this was particularly so just prior to the onset of these symptoms). I have put on weight and don't care much and am quite out of touch with my body . . . My face has a red rash around the mouth which is extending to blotchy lumps on the forehead and cheeks. This depresses me, and my eczema is steadily worsening.

Perhaps this is just a bad patch—an adjustment, but at present its weight is crushing me.

### 20th May
Today I wept for the wretched state of the world. Or was it myself I cried for? The world is a harsh, bleak place . . .

I have developed the bad habit of reading up on anxiety neuroses, and naturally the state of my own anxiety fluctuates according to whether what I read carries hope or not. Yes, it would appear that I am suffering from an anxiety neurosis—probably a mild one (though God forbid the experience of a severe one), because I don't have a focus for my anxiety although I have the symptoms alright. Anyway, having read that some anxiety neuroses vanish spontaneously, I have determined that mine is going to do just that!!! I will not spend my life as a neurotic—a mental and emotional cripple.

Because that is what these symptoms can lead to, their prime effect is to cut one off from the world and force one to live within the confines of the pre-occupied body, and no energy remains for anything or anyone else. How pathetic!

*3rd September*

. . . Not long after the last entry, this pathetic condition reached some sort of crisis. It was a long-weekend and the whole time I felt I was in conflict with my anxiety. I struggled to dismiss it, to ignore it, to control it—to no avail. And as the tension mounted, so too did my panic and the overwhelming feeling that I could no longer cope with it. Against my better judgment, I broke down and told S. (my partner) about it . . .

Since that time I have progressively improved. I have periodic relapses and the fear of its onset is, I suppose, never far from my mind, but on the whole it is quite manageable and I am—almost—normal again. Indeed, during a lengthy period of normalcy I almost forgot what the feelings of anxiety entailed. My major fear is that I know the anxiety cannot be *consciously* controlled and therefore can recommence at any time independently and against my will. I am, thus, at its mercy.

The commencement of my enforced leisure time has seen the reappearance of a number of symptoms which have persisted constantly, if not severely, over the past few days. My only means of dealing with them seems to be to attempt to ignore them, continue regardless, and attach as little significance as possible to them.

God I hope it works.

Mandy wrote, also, in a deeply personal way. Writing at the time she was responding to the questionnaire, hers was a reflection on the kinds of influences from her childhood that could have caused her to develop this severe anxiety condition, as well as other personal and interpersonal issues. While it has obviously been a painful exploration for her over the years, she admits it has helped her discover her 'real' self, and enabled her to develop 'a strong sense of independence'.

I suspect that my problem came from feeling unwanted and sexually unattractive.

While I lay no blame on my mother, she carried a child she didn't want and was forced to get married and stay in an unhappy marriage for sixteen years. I heard this 'officially' when I was about sixteen, when she left home. It disturbed me greatly, at the time. I believe a child can feel unwanted in the womb and I have carried this feeling all my life. It is a profound feeling of sadness.

There was no affection in our family and I missed out on all that 'normal' development. I tended in the early years to throw myself at men who were overwhelmed or uninterested, although I had a couple of early happy relationships, both of which I ended.

Most of my teenage years I felt ugly and sometimes when people mention 'ugly redheads', I still get hurt, although most of the time I think I look fairly attractive these days. I care more about letting the 'real me' come out now, instead of being obsessed with my looks. People respond to this, and I now have many good friends of both sexes.

On another issue, various places used to scare me. Crowded cafeterias (carrying trays was hard!), long corridors, walking in front of crowds of stationary people or in front of a lone person standing in a doorway. When working in a courthouse in Canberra I used to dread going to work every day because I'd have to walk in front of dozens of people sitting down.

Now, I still don't like these situations but I force myself to face them. The Tube corridors in London used to frighten me.

On the subject of men, I now feel that I look for more or less the right person—people who are good to me as well as being stimulating. Previously I used to choose safe bores or eccentric bastards. Now I have found a middle ground and I don't seem to have any trouble starting relationships, when I finally find someone I like! I don't feel like settling down or living with anyone. I have a strong sense of independence and I treat men as friends. I no longer take relationships so seriously.

## Some terms from psychological literature

Before we examine the work of particular scholars and clinicians on anxiety we will first consider more generally some of the terms used in psychological literature to describe severe anxiety, and some related terms—all in themselves very revealing.

### *Anxiety neurosis*

To distinguish the kind of severe anxiety which is non-specific and ever-present from normal anxiety, psychological literature uses terms like anxiety neurosis, neurotic anxiety or abnormal anxiety.

Remarks commonly made by doctors, psychologists and counsellors, as well as spouses and friends of anxiety-sufferers, such as 'We all get anxious sometimes' or 'A little bit of anxiety is good for us' or 'She's carrying it a bit too far', reveal a real ignorance about the difference between normal and neurotic anxiety. *Neurotic anxiety is not simply normal anxiety carried to the extreme!* It is a serious neurotic condition that is out of the control of the sufferer, and the sooner the rest of us understand and acknowledge that, the sooner we will stop blaming the sufferer for her condition.

### *Pervasive anxiety*

This is another term often used to describe the way in which this kind of anxiety pervades a person's whole life, never letting up, never giving the sufferer a moment's peace. Its effect is total. It takes away one's ability to relax, to enjoy one's own company, to have positive and happy thoughts about the future. It interferes with one's ability to enjoy one's spouse and children, to enjoy the company of friends, to interact with others without fear or guilt or self-recrimination. This kind of anxiety is so pervasive that no aspect of a sufferer's life escapes its effect.

### Free-floating anxiety and non-specific anxiety

These are commonly used and very apt terms for this non-specific cloud of anxiety that surrounds its sufferers and defies all logical explanation. In a strangely confusing way, the feelings of anxiety and panic are not found to be associated with anything specific. They are just there.

### Generalised anxiety disorder

This is a term used on the one hand to describe the non-specific nature of the anxiety, and on the other hand to distinguish it from other anxiety conditions that are more focused, such as phobias or obsessive/compulsive behaviour.

### Anxiety attack/panic attack

These terms describe the sudden appearance, for no apparent reason, of acute anxiety feelings. Going about one's normal routine, one can suddenly experience acute panic that is totally unrelated to anything one is doing or thinking about at the time.

So severe are these panic attacks that it only needs one such attack to ensure that a person will develop a fairly constant, free-floating anxiety. As a matter of fact, such anxiety feelings develop as a defence against another attack. The first one came from nowhere, gave no warning, and found its victim defenceless and vulnerable, and so she is determined she will never again be caught off guard. Adrenalin flowing constantly, the anxious person is never relaxed, always on guard, always ready, always waiting, always anticipating another attack.

What develops is anxiety about anxiety—not anxiety about something concrete as is the case with normal anxiety, but anxiety about anxiety, panic about panic, fear of fear.

Certain other terms are relevant here because of their very close relationship to the condition called anxiety neurosis. They are the terms phobia, agoraphobia and obsessive/compulsive neurosis.

### Phobia

A phobia is an irrational fear of something, developed as a way of containing or focusing one's anxiety. When the anxious person succeeds in developing a phobia, the anxiety is no longer experienced as free-floating or non-specific, because all of her anxiety can then be experienced in relation to this particular fear. The anxiety has been made specific, and because of its specificity the sufferer can then operate under the illusion that it is easier to handle. The problem is, of course, that anxiety almost always refuses to be contained in one phobia. The following example is typical of what can happen.

A woman develops a phobia about riding in buses, and she says to herself: 'If only I can avoid riding in buses, I'll be OK'. She feels relieved about that and her anxiety settles down. The problem is that one day she experiences an anxiety attack while driving her car, and immediately her phobia extends to driving cars. Then she decides she will only travel in a car as a passenger, until one day, she experiences a panic attack while riding as a passenger in her friend's car. This results in her having to narrow her existence even further. From now on, she will only ride in a car if her husband is driving . . . and so it goes on.

Anxiety very rarely, if ever, can be contained in one phobia, and yet the development of certain phobias does seem to be a very common response to free-floating anxiety and anxiety attacks. These include: fear of harming one's children, fear of confined spaces (claustrophobia), fear of staying home alone, fear of going out (agoraphobia), fear of being sick, fear of death, and fear of suicide.

Other phobias, usually referred to as simple phobias—fear of spiders, frogs, sharks, mice etc.—are different in that their origin and focus are more specific. Another notable difference is that while simple phobias cause a degree of discomfort, they usually have far less impact on a person's day-to-day functioning than do the phobias associated with anxiety neurosis.

### Agoraphobia

The phobia that is most closely related to anxiety neurosis is agoraphobia, and while the two terms are not synonymous as some would have us believe, it is not difficult to see how agoraphobia develops from free-floating anxiety. The term agoraphobia correctly means 'fear of the market-place' or 'fear of open spaces' or 'fear of going out'. Most anxiety-sufferers dread the thought of having an anxiety attack in a public place and if, as a consequence, they regularly choose to stay at home rather than go out, only then can they correctly be called agoraphobic.

A somewhat confusing situation has developed, though, in that 'agoraphobia' has come to be used to cover all situations involving panic attacks, even the situation one would presume to be the opposite of 'fear of the market-place', and that is, fear of staying home alone. It is important to see that while every agoraphobic experiences anxiety attacks, not everyone who suffers from anxiety attacks develops agoraphobia.

The relationship between neurotic anxiety and agoraphobia, then, can be said to be this: While neurotic anxiety is the primary condition, agoraphobia is a secondary condition that often, but not always, results from anxiety attacks.

### Obsessive/compulsive neurosis

This particular neurotic pattern, like other neuroses, is 'a technique for dealing with life and an attempt to achieve a sense of certainty in an uncertain world, to control oneself and one's surroundings, and to achieve physical and psychological protection from forces and events considered to be threatening' (Moore 1978, p. 34). In other words, obsessions and compulsions develop as attempts to ease anxiety caused by feelings of uncertainty, insecurity and powerlessness.

The obsessive person can find herself singing a song in her head over and over again sometimes for hours, or repeating a word over and over, and all efforts to fill her mind with other thoughts usually result in the tune or word returning with just as much force as before. The anxiety associated with obsessions is often relieved by the development of compulsive behaviour. The obsession: 'I didn't turn the iron off' is relieved by compulsive checking and rechecking. An obsession with tidiness is relieved by straightening and restraightening the cushions a hundred or more times a day.

31

Freud warned that it is important not to try to stop obsessive/ compulsive people performing their rituals because without those rituals, their anxiety would be unbearable. 'If we prevent a patient from carrying out a washing ceremonial, he falls into a state of anxiety which he finds hard to tolerate and from which he had evidently been protected by (the continual washing) . . .' (Freud 1964, p. 116). When such people are encouraged to take more control in those areas of their lives where they had previously felt powerless, and when they learn how to deal with their anxiety effectively, the obsessive/compulsive tendencies will ease of their own accord.

## Descriptions from the outside: scholars and clinicians describe anxiety

That which is said to be the earliest description of anxiety has come down to us from the early 19th century. Soren Kierkegaard, a Danish philosopher and theologian, wrote *The Concept of Dread* in 1844. Describing what Kierkegaard says about anxiety, the translator comments that the word 'dread' is important because it captures the essential element in Kierkegaard's writing, which is to define anxiety as 'an apprehension of the future, a pre-sentiment of a something which is "nothing" . . .' (Kierkegaard 1944, p. x). In other words, there is dread of something about to happen, but in fact there is nothing there.

Sigmund Freud, in his introductory lectures on psychoanalysis delivered in 1915–16, refers to neurotic anxiety as 'a freely floating, general apprehensiveness, ready to attach itself temporarily, in the form of what is known as "expectant anxiety", to any possibility that may freshly arise . . .' (Freud 1964, p. 114). In other words, once a person has experienced neurotic anxiety, she then lives in anticipation or expectancy of another attack.

Rollo May, writing in 1950, in his book *The Meaning of Anxiety,* says 'It is agreed by students of anxiety . . . that anxiety is a diffuse apprehension, and that the difference between fear and anxiety is that fear is a reaction to a specific danger while anxiety is unspecific, "vague", "objectless" ' (May 1950, p. 205).

This brief look at how scholars such as Kierkegaard, Freud and May have described the condition is important, but there are two clinicians I want to quote more extensively. They are Dr Claire Weekes, a doctor who is recognised throughout the western world as an authority on the treatment of nervous illness, and Dr Larry Evans, a psychiatrist who has done extensive work in Australia with patients suffering from agoraphobia in particular.

Dr Claire Weekes wrote her important book *Self Help for your Nerves* in 1962. Throughout the book she uses the term 'nervous breakdown' to describe severe anxiety, a term which I must admit I find fairly awkward these days simply because nobody really knows exactly what it means, and it seems to conjure up in people's minds some dreaded state from which there is no return. Whenever people start therapy by saying: 'I think I'm having a nervous breakdown', a therapist ought always to ask what that means to them. Many people say it as if it is the 'end of the road', a state of hopelessness, a point of no return when in fact, as Dr Weekes explains, 'a nervous breakdown is no more than an intensification of (nervousness) . . . a state in which a person's "nervous" symptoms are so intense that he copes inadequately with his daily work or does not cope at all' (Weekes 1962, p. 6). The important point to remember is that it is not a person's nerves that break down, but rather his or her ability to cope with daily work and responsibilities.

## Physical and emotional symptoms

Dr Weekes gives a fairly full description of the physical and emotional symptoms of severe anxiety, as follows:

> People suffering from . . . (anxiety neurosis), complain of some, or all, of the following symptoms of sensitized involuntary nerves: sleeplessness, depression, fatigue, churning stomach, indigestion, racing heart, banging heart, shaking heart, palpitations, 'missed' heart-beats, a sharp knife-like pain under the heart, a sore feeling around the heart, sweating hands, 'pins and needles' in the hands and feet, a choking feeling in the throat, an inability to take a deep breath, a tight feeling across the chest, 'ants' or 'worms' crawling under the skin, a tight band of pain around the head,

giddiness, and strange tricks of vision such as the apparent movement of inanimate objects. Nausea, vomiting, occasional diarrhoea, and frequent desire to pass urine may be added to the picture (Weekes 1962, p. 8).

Then she goes on to say:

Sufferers from these symptoms . . . are quite certain that there is something seriously wrong with them and cannot believe that anyone else could have had such a distressing experience. Many feel convinced that they have a brain tumour . . . or that they are on the verge of madness. Their one wish is to be, as quickly as possible, the person they used to be before this 'horrible thing' happened to them. They are often not aware that their symptoms are nervous in origin and follow a well-recognized pattern shared by numerous sufferers like themselves, *the pattern of continuous fear and tension* (Weekes 1962, p. 9).

Weekes speaks about a 'fear–adrenalin–fear cycle', and uses an example of a man who becomes fearful after experiencing his first unexpected attack of heart palpitations. Even a healthy heart experiences palpitations at times and most of us just go about what we are doing and pay it little attention. This man, however, was convinced he was about to have a heart attack and became afraid.

Fear causes an additional outpouring of adrenalin, so that a heart already stirred to palpitations becomes further excited, beats even more quickly and the attack lasts longer. The sufferer may panic, thinking he is about to die. His hands sweat, his face burns, his fingers tingle with 'pins and needles', while he waits for he knows not what.

The attack eventually stops . . . However, having had one frightening experience, he dreads another and for days remains tense and anxious . . .

. . . It is not long before tension, releasing more and more adrenalin, makes his stomach churn, his hands sweat and his heart constantly beat quickly. He becomes even more afraid, and still more adrenalin is released. In other words, he becomes caught in the fear–adrenalin–fear cycle (Weekes 1962, p. 10).

She speaks of the person who 'dreads being alone "for fear of having a turn"; (yet who) at the same time . . . is afraid to be with people for fear of having one and making a fool of himself' (Weekes 1962, p. 11). Again, she paints a picture of someone who has to:

> . . . fight through almost every waking moment, with sweating hands and tensed muscles, agitatedly trying to force forgetfulness of his desperate state by consciously concentrating on other things. Or he may pace the floor of his mind, anxiously searching for a way out of his miserable prison, only to find one closed door after another (Weekes 1962, p. 14).

Dr Weekes' descriptions help those of us who have never experienced this type of severe anxiety to gain some insight into the agony and torment and self-alienation anxiety-sufferers experience, while those who have experienced it will identify immediately with the feelings she describes. A brief outline of Dr Weekes' treatment method can be found in chapter 6 (pp. 145–6).

Dr Larry Evans, Associate Professor of Psychiatry at the University of Sydney, delivered a paper in the early 1980s called Agoraphobia: Answers to a few Questions. In it, he gives a fairly thorough description of the physical symptoms of the anxiety which causes agoraphobia. He speaks of:

> . . . a feeling of light-headedness or a feeling of being detached from your surroundings . . . Other symptoms which commonly occur are—a buzzing in the ears, blurring of vision and a dry mouth. Some people find it difficult to breathe and they catch their breath or even breathe very heavily or rapidly . . . After a time the person who is over-breathing will start to feel a bit light-headed and they'll get a tingling in their arms and legs . . .
>   Other symptoms . . . are pains in the chest and palpitations . . . a number of people . . . also have trouble with their digestion and they have . . . gastro-intestinal symptoms . . . Some people even have what we call irritable bowel syndrome . . .
>   The milder symptoms are a feeling of churning in the stomach . . . pain in the stomach . . . indigestion and

sometimes . . . severe and frequent diarrhoea. They
occasionally tremble and their muscles will sometimes twitch
. . . Some agoraphobics suffer from aches and pains . . .
headaches . . . migraine . . . (Evans undated, p. 2).

The descriptions in this chapter from 'inside' and 'outside' the
experience of severe anxiety make it very clear that we are not
dealing here with a condition that could be called normal
anxiety or stress or fear. At an emotional level, far from being an
experience of stress or fear it is, in fact, an experience of terror,
horror, panic, dread, apprehension, a feeling of impending col-
lapse or even death. At a physical level, too, the symptoms are
not just normal physical symptoms that accompany stress or fear.
Rather they are inexplicable bodily disturbances that signal to
the sufferer serious physical illness and possible death. How does
neurotic anxiety differ from stress and fear?

## Anxiety and stress: a comparison

It must be made clear that anxiety is *not* stress. Those who equate
anxiety with stress are doing a great disservice to anxiety-
sufferers, because they paint a picture of someone whose condition is, to a large degree, their own fault, someone who has
allowed the stress to build up and who refuses or is unable to
reduce the stress in their lives. This is simply not a true picture,
and such a suggestion only serves to lay an added burden on
anxiety-sufferers, most of whom are only too willing to blame
themselves for what they already feel is a 'weakness of character'.

What is stress? Stress is a term borrowed from engineering
and physics, which has become popular in psychology in recent
years as a way of talking about what happens at a personal level
when people overload themselves with work or worry or guilt.
Stress occurs, we are told, when force or pressure is applied to
something. Many of life's experiences place people under considerable pressure and have the potential for causing a great deal
of stress. Examples of such experiences are: the death of a family
member or close friend; the break-up of a relationship; losing a
job; moving house; the outbreak of war; natural disasters,
environmental disasters; being the victim of violence, torture,

36

terrorist activities; being made homeless; and so on.

An important difference between the terms stress and anxiety is that 'stress' tends to put the emphasis on something happening *to* the person from the outside, whereas 'anxiety' refers to something happening *within* the person. There is beneficial stress and harmful stress. The kind of pressure that motivates me to eat something when I am hungry is a beneficial stress, while the kind of pressure that overloads me with too much work when I am tired is a harmful stress.

Highly stressed people will display some or all of the following symptoms, taken from a Queensland Department of Health booklet on stress (note that many of these symptoms are similar to those experienced by anxiety-sufferers, which probably accounts for much of the misdiagnosis that occurs):

- irritability
- depression
- dryness of the throat and mouth
- pounding heart
- overpowering urge to cry
- inability to concentrate
- fatigue, exhaustion
- free-floating anxiety
- trembling, nervous tics
- high-pitched, nervous laugh
- grinding of teeth
- stuttering or stumbling over words
- insomnia
- sweating
- frequent need to urinate
- diarrhoea
- headaches
- premenstrual tension, or missed periods
- pain in the lower back and neck
- loss of appetite or excessive appetite
- increased smoking

- increased use of alcohol and/or drugs
- muddled dreams, nightmares
  (Queensland Department of Health, undated, p. 1).

When a person is suffering from stress, there is usually an obvious stressor or cause, but with anxiety there is not. Common causes of stress are:

- frustrations, insults, assaults, demands
- unresolved problems from the past that continually play on one's mind
- being in a relationship that is not working
- absence of communication, or poor communication
- inability or unwillingness to be assertive
- being in the wrong job
- feelings of being trapped
- feelings of guilt
- feelings of powerlessness
- loneliness
- boredom

To lower one's stress level, one needs to discover what the stressor (cause) is and work at eliminating it. While this strategy is very effective in dealing with stress, it does not work with anxiety. Nevertheless, most people suffering from anxiety symptoms do try in the initial stages at least to discover a cause for their anxiety, in the mistaken belief that their symptoms will be relieved when they can eliminate the cause. Such action is usually reinforced by the advice of well-meaning doctors, therapists, family members and friends. With anxiety, any such search for a cause as a means of relieving the symptoms is pointless, and only serves to create more anxiety. Any enquiry into cause will only be helpful if undertaken *after* an anxiety-sufferer has overcome her anxiety by following the treatment process set out in chapter 6.

Another feature contributing to misdiagnosis is the fact that 'stress' and 'burn-out' have become such fashionable terms in recent years, and consequently, it seems much more acceptable to be suffering from stress than from anxiety.

While anxiety is not stress and stress is not anxiety, there is nevertheless some relationship between the two, and it is important to clarify this. Anxiety can and does cause stress. A person who suffers from anxiety is usually also highly stressed as a result of trying to deal with her anxiety on a daily basis. Stress, on the other hand, does not cause the condition we are calling severe anxiety. The part stress plays in anxiety is simply to exacerbate an already existing condition. Anxiety-sufferers are well advised, therefore, to keep their stress levels down as much as possible by involving themselves in a healthy diet and exercise program, making sure they get enough sleep, working on and resolving relationship problems, eliminating boredom and loneliness as much as possible and adhering to manageable work hours and practices.

| STRESS | ANXIETY |
|---|---|
| Occurs when pressure is applied | Occurs out of nowhere—does not appear to be related to anything specific |
| Happens *to* the person from the outside | Happens *within* the person |
| Usually has an obvious cause | Has no obvious cause |
| Can be lowered or eliminated by finding the cause | Is made worse by focusing on a search for a cause |
| Does not cause anxiety but makes already existing anxiety harder to handle | Does cause stress levels to rise |
| Responds to treatment at a behavioural level | Responds to treatment involving acceptance and self-talk |

## Anxiety and fear: a comparison

One point of disagreement I have with some Behaviour therapists is that they often equate anxiety with fear, and as a consequence of that, the method of treatment they use with anxiety-sufferers is often the same as the method they have found effective in the treatment of fears or phobias. In working with phobias it is very important to help a person identify her fear and slowly encourage her to become more familiar with the feared object. In this way, she will, over time, become desensitised to the object of her fear and her phobia will disappear. In working with anxiety, however, there is no one thing that makes a person anxious, rather she feels anxious about everything and nothing, and therefore any attempt at desensitisation or behaviour-change is pointless. If a therapist pushes hard enough, an anxiety-sufferer will come up with something she thinks might be causing her anxiety (often just to please the therapist!), but even after they work on it together, the anxiety itself will not be relieved in any permanent sense.

While fear is always involved in anxiety, anxiety is not fear. Freud discussed the difference in his *New Introductory Lectures on Psychoanalysis*. Fear arises in response to an external danger, he said, while anxiety develops in relation to an internal danger made more complicated and difficult because it is not consciously recognised. He said: 'One can save oneself from an external danger by flight; fleeing from an internal danger is a difficult enterprise' (Freud 1964, p. 117).

Rollo May also makes a comparison between anxiety and fear, as mentioned earlier. He said: 'the central difference between fear and anxiety is that fear is a reaction to a specific danger while anxiety is unspecific, "vague", "objectless"' (May 1950, p. 205). In fear, one knows what one is afraid of and can choose either fight or flight, but anxiety is experienced at a much deeper level. 'One *has* a fear', he says, but 'One *is* anxious' (May 1950, p. 207).

The relationship between fear and anxiety, according to May, is that anxiety comes first, and fear develops as a result of the

| FEAR | ANXIETY |
|---|---|
| Arises in response to an obvious external danger | Arises in response to an internal danger which cannot be consciously recognised |
| Evokes the response of fight or flight | Is experienced at a much deeper level and cannot be eased by fight or flight |
| Is a reaction to a specific danger | Is unspecific, vague, objectless |
| Is secondary to anxiety—an expression of underlying anxiety | Is primary, and is sometimes expressed in fears or phobias |
| Responds to treatment at a behavioural level | Responds to treatment involving acceptance and self-talk |

underlying anxiety. Neurotic fears or phobias develop out of neurotic anxiety, in the same way as normal fears develop out of normal anxiety. 'A neurotic fear is a specific, differentiated, objectivated expression of underlying neurotic anxiety' (May 1950, pp. 224–5).

## Changes after the first anxiety attack

A situation many anxiety-sufferers find difficult to accept is that after their first anxiety attack, life is never the same again. Significant changes take place both in their relationships and in themselves, and no description of anxiety would be complete without comment on these changes.

### Changes in relationships

Relationships change, not only because the anxiety-sufferer herself is different but also because of the way her partner reacts to her condition and therefore to her. Initially the partner, like the sufferer herself, has absolutely no understanding of what is happening. After the initial confusion, most partners respond in one of the following three ways. First, those who do not usually pay attention to how their partner is feeling just continue in the same vein. Any attempt the sufferer makes to tell her partner about her anxiety is ignored.

Second, there are many who do seem to care in the beginning, but they quickly tire of it. It often goes like this: The first time an anxiety-sufferer talks about her feelings of anxiety, panic, terror, her partner listens and is genuinely concerned. She is held and reassured and told 'there's nothing to be afraid of'. She feels a little better, relaxes and goes off to sleep. In the morning when she wakes, she feels anxious again and tries to talk to her partner, but this time she senses some impatience. Generally speaking, though, there is concern and a fair degree of support for the first week or two. After that, she begins to be chastised for being 'silly', and gets a very clear message that 'enough is enough'.

Some partners seem to feel that all they need to do is give the right advice, and if the advice is adhered to the problem will go away. If the problem does not go away it means the advice has not been followed, and the partner then feels justified in being annoyed. The stereotype of women as weak and nervous is reinforced and there is annoyance at the thought that the sufferer is becoming one of those stereotypic women. Often there is irritation because what is seen as the sufferer's weakness, nervousness and potential dependence may interfere with the partner's own plans. So, without attempting to understand the devastating experience the anxiety-sufferer is going through, many partners set about making it clear that all she needs to do is pull herself together and show some strength of character.

Third, there is a somewhat smaller group who actually enjoy the feeling that comes with involvement in a relationship with someone who seems to fit the stereotype. Such partners usually respond to the sufferer's anxiety by encouraging her to be more and more dependent. As much as is humanly possible, the whole of life is organised around her anxiety. Her partner is always there for her, driving her wherever she wants to go, waiting for her, making sure she is not alone, and so on. While this attitude appears commendable, it is, in fact, not a healthy one, and tends to reveal as much about the partner's need as it does about the anxiety-sufferer's.

Any one of these responses—ignoring her feelings altogether, showing impatience with what is labelled a 'weakness of character', or encouraging her to become dependent—causes a woman to feel misunderstood and alienated, and from that moment on there is an emotional distance between the couple that has a significant long-term effect on the relationship. Many observers would blame the anxiety for the change in the relationship, when more correctly it is the partner's response to the anxiety that has caused the relationship to change.

### Changes within the anxiety-sufferer

There are also changes that occur in the anxiety-sufferer herself. These are changes that effect her emotional state, her self-esteem, her attitude to herself, as well as her attitude to the world in general. Where once she felt reasonably good about

42

herself and the world, she now feels alienated, helpless, weak, terrified, irrational, out of control, preoccupied with herself, hypochondriachal, fearful of going crazy and powerless to do anything to restore her former confidence in herself and the world. Her life seems out of her hands, and though there may be people around her who care, there is nobody who has any understanding of what she is going through. Such changes that occur within herself, together with the distance she feels in her relationships, usually cause an anxiety-sufferer to feel very much alone and adrift.

## What kinds of people develop severe anxiety?

There are many misconceptions about the kinds of people who become anxiety-sufferers. In an article written in 1968 in *The Medical Journal of Australia,* the author describes what he calls 'a typical story' of someone suffering from anxiety neurosis.

> Investigation of a woman . . . may show that in early childhood she was over-timid with other children or strangers, prone perhaps to nightmares, or unduly fearful of the dark. In adolescence, such events as school examinations or her first social outings produced almost a state of panic. She might then have married a partly incompatible husband, sexual adjustment might not have been entirely satisfactory . . . (Prendergast 1968, p. 598).

While the author expresses all this in the mode of conjecture, it does, nevertheless, reveal some of the misunderstanding of the condition prevalent in the medical profession at that time, a lack of understanding which is still evident in some quarters today. The suggestions that anxiety-sufferers were over-timid as children and teenagers, or that in adulthood they are all in unhappy or incompatible relationships are simply not able to be substantiated, but such suggestions from the past do have an effect on our assumptions about anxiety-sufferers today.

Some other misconceptions are that they are people of low intelligence, people who are 'weak-willed', or people who have an inordinate amount of time on their hands to spend in needless self-preoccupation. In an attempt to address some of this errone-ous information, we need to ask: What kind of person is likely to develop severe anxiety? What is known about the number and type of people experiencing this condition?

*At this time in history, more people are suffering from anxiety disor-ders than from any other mental disorder.* A study carried out in 1988 in the United States reveals: 'Anxiety disorders . . . were the most prevalent of all the major groups of mental disorders. Within this group, phobic disorders were the most common . . . followed by obsessive-compulsive disorder . . . and panic disorder . . .' (Regier et al. 1988, p. 981).

Statistics show that *twice as many women as men* suffer with anxiety. When considering such a finding, however, there are two facts that need to be kept in mind. One is that statistics are usually based on those who seek treatment, and women are much more likely than men to seek treatment for an emotional problem. The other is that men are much more likely than women to turn to alcohol as a way of dealing with anxiety, and when their drinking becomes excessive, their problem is then seen to be alcoholism rather than anxiety. The above-mentioned enquiry into the prevalence of mental disorders revealed: 'Men have significantly higher rates of substance use disorders and antisocial personality disorder. In contrast, women have signifi-cantly higher rates of affective, anxiety, and somatization disor-ders' (Regier et al. 1988, p. 985). There is no way of knowing, at this stage, what percentage of men seen to have an alcohol abuse problem are actually using alcohol to mask a deeper anxiety problem.

Anxiety-sufferers *come from all social, economic and educational levels.* A look at the different lifestyle choices available to women in western society reveals that severe anxiety exists among hap-pily and unhappily married, single, separated and divorced women, lesbians, those who are mothers and those who are not, those women who have chosen traditional lifestyles as well as those who have chosen alternative lifestyles. It is found amongst the wealthy, the middle-income earners and the poor alike.

Regarding educational levels, some research indicates it is more prevalent among women who achieve higher educational standards than those who have not had the same opportunities, but again, a significant variable is the fact that people of average and above average education are probably more likely to seek help from a therapist, and are consequently more likely to be included in the statistics.

Far from the mistaken belief that anxiety-sufferers are people who have a lot of time on their hands, therapists find it is *often people who are living busy, productive lives* who suddenly find themselves overcome by an anxiety attack.

The condition *often exists in several generations of the same family.* When that fact is discovered, it naturally gives rise to the speculation that this is a genetic or hereditary condition, but there is no indication that this is so. Rather, the explanation for its showing up in several generations seems to be that of learned responses. This will be dealt with in more detail in later chapters on cause.

Because severe anxiety is such a hidden condition, it is often the case that different family members are suffering from anxiety without each other's knowledge. All the shame and guilt attached to the condition, the feeling that it is just an overwhelming weakness, causes people to go to great lengths to hide it even from those closest to them. When an anxiety-sufferer begins to learn about the condition and understands that it is nothing to be ashamed of, and when she eventually finds the courage to talk about it to other family members, she often discovers then that one of her parents has battled with the same problem for years.

While some people experience their first anxiety attack in their teenage years, and some in their thirties and forties, *the majority of people have their first attack in their twenties* (Moore 1978, pp. 17–18).

An anxiety-sufferer is *more often than not a person who is very pleasant.* Apart from times of high anxiety when her response is usually to withdraw and go into herself, she is generally someone who smiles a lot, seeks to please, strives to be positive, and finds it difficult to criticise (particularly close family members). She has a low self-esteem, although that is not always apparent on the surface. She feels inordinately guilty about almost everything. In fact, she always seems to be ready to take the blame, and finds it remarkably easy to feel guilty. While she can be very assertive in some areas of her life, she is particularly unassertive in others (again, usually in situations involving close family members).

An anxiety-sufferer *often feels invisible*. It is not uncommon for an anxiety-sufferer to have the feeling of being left out, passed by, ignored, betrayed or abandoned, and such experiences leave her feeling absolutely desolated.

This description of severe anxiety, presented through the words of anxiety-sufferers themselves as well as those who have written about it in a more objective, clinical way, has painted a clear picture of what this condition is that causes its sufferers to feel totally devastated and so totally out of control of their own lives.

Those readers who are looking for immediate relief from their anxiety are urged to turn now to chapter 6 and follow very closely the treatment steps outlined there. It is imperative that you begin to put those steps into practice immediately and let the cure begin. Whatever you do, be careful not to stand in the way of your own cure by continuing to struggle with your condition. Give up on trying to control it and you will notice a difference immediately. Then, when you feel ready, you may want to return to this point and read the chapters you missed.

Those who are reading straight through will see that the next four chapters are devoted to the question of cause. Chapter 2 deals with the issue of women's anxiety in a broader social context. In it, we take a detailed look at society and its attitude to women in an attempt to discover what it is that causes so many women in western countries to experience this kind of deep and traumatic anxiety.

Chapters 3, 4 and 5 then return to a discussion of possible causes of anxiety in individual women. The intention of these four chapters is to show that anxiety in individual women is very much influenced by the fact that they live in a society that deprives women in general of any kind of real control over their lives.

For immediate relief from anxiety symptoms, turn now to chapter 6. The intervening chapters can be read at a later date.

# 2

# The age of anxiety—for women

THE personal stories in chapter 1 reveal that when a woman is in the grip of an anxiety attack, or when she is unable to rid herself of constant, free-floating anxiety day after day, she feels helplessly out of control of her own life.

Because that feeling of helplessness is present much of the time, 'control' becomes the focus of an anxiety-sufferer's attention even when she feels less anxious. During those times of relief, she attempts to exercise control by structuring her life—and sometimes the lives of the people around her—so as to minimise the chances of the anxiety returning. But *control is always a difficult issue for anxiety-sufferers who are women.* Their struggle for control is a double struggle: first, because they are women in a society where men have all the control; and second, because they are anxiety-sufferers. Any effort at control made by an anxiety-sufferer who happens to be a woman, is made more difficult by the fact that she is first a woman. It is therefore imperative, when trying to understand the condition of severe anxiety in women, that we look at the issue of control and lack of control as it relates to all women in male-dominated, male-oriented western societies.

In such societies, women can be said to lack control by virtue of the fact that all the *real* control is in the hands of the men. The very way in which those societies have been constructed ensures that the opportunities for men to achieve control at personal and social levels are maximised, while the opportunities for women are virtually non-existent.

It is for that reason that this age in which we live, while variously referred to as 'the technological age', 'the nuclear age', 'the age of the computer' and so on can rightly be called 'the age of opportunity' for men, but for women it is 'the age of anxiety'.

Later in this chapter, we will look at what the term 'age of anxiety' means and ask questions like: How have women in modern western societies arrived at the age of anxiety? What are the psychological stages women as a group have come through prior to arriving at this stage? What is it about this particular period that distinguishes it from other periods in women's recent history so as to warrant the name age of anxiety? How are women responding to their collective anxiety? Before turning to these questions, however, it is important that we look first at how it all started.

## Lack of control: the root cause of women's anxiety

Women's collective experience of powerlessness and absence of control over their own lives is at the root of every individual woman's experience of severe anxiety. To put it another way, anxiety in individual women develops out of the sense of powerlessness, invisibility and emotional deprivation experienced by all women in a society which still chooses to treat them with contempt for no other reason than that they are women.

It must be emphasised here that while society's treatment of women is seen to be the root cause of severe anxiety, it is not the *only* cause. If it were, then there would exist a situation where all women suffered from the condition and all men did not. That this is clearly not the case leads us to examine other causal factors in subsequent chapters. What is being suggested here is that, due to their experience of powerlessness, all women have the potential for developing the condition in a way that all men do not.

If you are a woman and an anxiety-sufferer you are urged, as you read this chapter, to open your eyes and allow yourself to see the process all women go through in a male-dominated society, because such insight will provide you with a background to

49

understanding the development of your own particular anxiety condition. While, for many, the following discussion of the unequal treatment of girls and boys will simply be a confirmation of a situation you have been aware of for some time, it is nevertheless important to repeat it here as a reminder of how women's lack of control begins.

The process actually begins with a woman's entry at birth into a society which automatically deprives her of control over her own life and ends, in the majority of cases, with that woman actually giving up control of her life to others because the daily struggle to maintain even a small degree of control has proved too difficult. At least five steps can be identified in the process.

## Conditioning of girls and boys

First, there is the socialisation process by which both girls and boys are conditioned from the moment of birth to ensure that they fit neatly into the roles society has prepared for them. In order that boys are given every opportunity to begin on the road to success and fulfilment, they are encouraged to be outspoken, independent, ambitious, creative, aggressive and self-focused. Girls, on the other hand, are encouraged to be quiet, dependent, pleasant, attractive, conforming and caring (other-focused).

A boy's socialisation teaches him that he is at the centre of life, while a girl learns that her role is to relate to and take care of the one at the centre. She is the support-person, the helper, the one who is always to be there for everyone else. Simone de Beauvoir, in *The Second Sex,* alerted us to the fact that that is the way most men see their relationship to women. Consciously or unconsciously, man relates to himself as 'subject' and to woman as 'the other'. It is not readily apparent that he perceives woman as a person in her own right, rather he sees her as the one whose task it is to relate to him, the subject, without any thought of becoming a subject herself (de Beauvoir, 1952).

Childhood conditioning is so successful that most women have no reason to suspect any injustice at all till they begin to experience at a personal level the oppression inherent in the system. Even then, the injustice is not something women immediately recognise. Most women just have a sense of being dissatisfied with their lives and because that feeling is not easy to explain, they often blame themselves for 'wanting too much out of life'. The fact is, most women simply want what is rightfully theirs—the chance to be as fully as possible who they really are. It is the conditioning that takes place in childhood that robs a woman of that opportunity, because girls in our society are conditioned into powerlessness. Such conditioning takes place in three main ways: through observing one's parents, through sexrole expectations, and through other damaging childhood experiences.

From very early in life, a girl *observes her own parents* and sees that fathers are bigger and stronger, mothers are smaller and weaker; fathers do important work, mothers cook and clean; fathers come home tired and worn out and must not be disturbed, mothers are always at home when the children are there, and can be disturbed at any time. From these early observations, she learns that men (and what men do) are much more important than women (and what women do).

In the interpersonal area, a girl observing her parents learns that when there are other adults around fathers do the talking, mothers do the listening; fathers interrupt or talk over others, mothers can be interrupted or talked over; fathers have opinions which must be taken seriously, mothers do not have opinions, or if they do, their opinions are ignored or trivialised. From these observations, she learns that men must be smarter and more interesting than women.

Again, she observes that when there are no other adults around mothers want to talk, fathers watch TV; mothers plead, fathers ignore; mothers cry, fathers get annoyed; mothers get frustrated and angry, fathers walk out or become violent. From these observations, she easily concludes that women are irrational, women are to blame when relationships go wrong, while men have a lot to endure and deserve sympathy.

In addition to all a girl learns about women's powerlessness from observing her parents' interactions—that is, women are not important, women are not interesting, women are not smart, women are responsible for everything that goes wrong—her conditioning continues *through sex-role expectations* both inside and outside the home. Boys, both at home and at school, are given much more time and attention than girls. In fact, girls usually get what is left over after boys have been attended to. Rebellious behaviour, often tolerated in boys, is usually punished in girls, while compliant behaviour in girls is rewarded. Girls learn quite early in life that being good and kind and pleasant gets the best response from adults.

Another method society uses to ensure that girls are conditioned into powerlessness is the emphasis placed on the helper/carer role. Girls are given dolls at a young age and encouraged to play with them, care for them, bathe, feed and clothe them, nurse them to sleep and so on. Helping with the housework, cooking meals, taking responsibility for younger brothers and sisters, comforting one or both parents when they are down, all of these are helping/caring tasks that are more often than not expected of girls in a family, rather than boys.

In recent years, more and more parents have been making a determined effort not to perpetuate the stereotypes in the raising of their children. Having freed themselves to a large extent from their own conditioning, both mother and father are confident that they are doing all they can to set an example for their children that will enable them to be free of sex-role expectations and conditioning. The frustration for many such parents, however, is that, due to the influence of school and the media, their children seem to learn the stereotypes almost automatically. School is still a very powerful vehicle of socialisation. Through education department material and teaching methods as well as pressure from their peers, children are forced into contact with sex-role stereotypes every day. The influence of the media, too, is very strong. Television, in particular, is a powerful tool of socialisation through which children are conditioned into the accepted stereotypes.

With reference to *damaging childhood experiences*, without a doubt, the most damaging of all is the conditioning of girls into powerlessness through sexual abuse. Sexual abuse of children by father, step-father, grandfather, older brother or any other adult is a most serious abuse of adult power and causes the victim to experience a lasting sense of powerlessness. Although boys are sexually abused, too, by their fathers and other men, overwhelmingly the victims of sexual abuse are girls.

### Growing awareness of injustice

Whatever their experiences in life, most girls repress their feelings of dissatisfaction and fear and anger because, in their powerlessness, there seem to be few, if any, options. They grow up and, in line with society's expectations, they fall in love, get married and have children of their own. Then, as a result of conditioning, a woman finds herself in adult life in a situation where she is responsible for everyone else's life (husband, children, parents and so on). She is concerned for their happiness, their successes, their fulfilment, and pays little, if any, attention to her own. It seems that she is supposed to live for everyone else so that they can go on living for themselves.

At one level she feels it is her duty to live for others, while at another level she experiences the situation as acutely unjust. What it means in practice is that they control her by making constant demands on her which, out of duty, she feels she cannot reject. She has been taught right from the beginning of her life that everyone else's happiness depends on her staying in this role, and also that it is in this role that she will find fulfilment and meaning.

### Growing dissatisfaction combined with guilt

Any woman who allows herself to consider her situation will become aware sooner or later that while she lives for everyone else and everyone else lives for themselves, there is no-one living for her, and at that point she experiences a growing dissatisfaction. Who she is has become lost. By doing what a woman is expected to do, she has lost her true self. Special events in life, such as her youngest child starting school, first child leaving home, last child leaving home, her 40th birthday, cause her to examine her life and wonder what she has achieved for herself, and the answer usually is—very little. Her life has been other-directed rather than self-directed. She has spent years doing what she knew others expected of her and very little for herself, and now she is experiencing dissatisfaction, and sometimes anger.

The feeling of dissatisfaction with one's life is usually a healthy feeling because it is often the catalyst for change and growth, but most women who begin to feel dissatisfied with their lives also experience a fair degree of guilt, and guilt has a way of convincing them they have no right to feel dissatisfied. There is guilt about feeling dissatisfied, guilt about feeling unfulfilled, guilt about wanting to change their lives but not knowing how to go about it, and guilt because when a woman decides to do something for herself, it is called 'selfish'.

### Growing awareness of emptiness and meaninglessness

When a woman looks at her life and sees nothing apart from her partner and children, she realises her life only has meaning as she lives it through them. There is no meaning which is her very own. Even when she does achieve something for herself, no value is placed on it by herself or anyone else. She is a woman controlled by society's expectations—caregiver, nurturer, peacemaker— selflessly accepting whatever knocks come her way, absorbing emotional and psychological abuse, always ready to give up her own interests and desires to fit in with the interests and desires of partner and children. Who she is and what she wants is not important. This path of self-denial which was supposed to be the path that led to real fulfilment and meaning for women, does, in truth, lead to a frightening sense of emptiness and meaninglessness.

### Negative self-image, low self-esteem

A woman who lives her life within the narrowly defined expectations of male-oriented society will develop a negative self-image. She will place the same value on herself as society places on all women, and consequently her self-esteem will be very low. Our society is full of young women, middle-aged women and older women with low self-esteem, lacking in confidence, desperately looking for affirmation, taking anti-depressants, who look back sometimes at the bright, happy, confident younger

54

women they imagine they once were, and wonder what happened.

What happened was that they did what society expected them to do and lived their lives for others instead of living for themselves. They were not told that that would lead to emptiness, meaninglessness, low self-esteem, depression, powerlessness and a lack of any sense of real control over their own lives. Such lack of control is the root cause of the anxiety all women live with.

Since the beginning of time, or at least since the writer of Genesis decided to blame Eve for Adam's sin, women have been deprived of any real control over their lives. Even those relatively few women throughout history who have rebelled and insisted on being 'subject' rather than 'other', have had a sense of somehow still being controlled even in their rebelliousness. Consequently, it could be said that every age has been an age of anxiety for women, but there are clear reasons why this present time in the history of western society is more deserving than all the others of that label, and it is important that we turn our attention to that now. First, we will look at how traditional historians have named the ages through which civilisation has progressed since the first few centuries AD. Second, we will develop a new naming of women's experiences with particular reference to the most recent period, that is, the 19th and 20th centuries.

## The ages of man

In the past, any comment on the stages through which humanity has progressed has always been done in terms of men's experience rather than women's.

### The Dark Ages

When historians call the period between about the 5th and 10th centuries the Dark Ages, they go on to refer only to the exploits of the men of the time—constant warfare, invasions, migrations, which caused political fragmentation and economic decay. If this period were named according to the experience of the women of the day who had to contend with such male behaviour, it might be called something like the *age of despair.*

## *The age of faith*

Another familiar term from history is the term Middle Ages, which refers loosely to the period from about the 6th to the 15th or 16th centuries. The period from the 11th century on is often called the High Middle Ages or the Later Middle Ages, or according to church historians, the age of faith. This was the period in which the church expanded and flourished, and theological teaching became more influential than ever, but for women, it was a time when any influence they may have had in the past was taken away. 'Church writings showed a greater tendency to regard women as the "other", the basis for a growing misogyny and a violation of the orthodox christian belief that all souls, without distinction of age, class, or sex, are equal in the eyes of God' (French 1985, p. 154).

The great reforms of the church deliberately excluded women, even from educational roles.

> All leadership roles for women in the Church were precluded as the center of policy making shifted from the monastic system to Rome and the papacy. At this time the great cathedral schools were being established; they quickly became centers of an explosion of learning and debate. Women were completely excluded from these schools, and not even the priest's wife, once a familiar figure in religious institutions, appeared in them. Both the students and the staff were required to be celibate males (French 1985, p. 154).

The following is a much-quoted excerpt from a 'kindly book', written in 1392–94 by an elderly man for his child wife, setting out her duty toward her husband:

> The wife, he says, should be like a little dog who remains near its master always and avoids other people, who thinks of nothing but its master even when the master is away, who waits at home for his return and follows him whenever it is permitted. If the master whips the dog or throws stones at it, the dog wags its tail, lies down before him, licks his hand and attempts to mollify him (French 1985, pp. 156–7).

For women, it could have been an age of freedom and hope, but under the influence of Christian teaching, it was an *age of subjugation*.

## The age of reason

Following the age of faith and influenced by the Renaissance (14th to 16th centuries) came the age of reason. Beginning in the 17th century and flourishing in the 18th, the Enlightenment was a revolutionary movement that questioned the authority of religious tradition, and sought to emphasise the value of reason in religion. Absolute faith gave way to a spirit of doubt and criticism. The period of the Enlightenment was a period of great progress for all—except women.

> (It) is considered a progressive and rational period, an age of light and reason. It gave birth to stirring assertions of the equality and brotherhood of man, to Rousseau's powerful proclamation that although man is everywhere in chains, he is born free. The *philosophes* set out to achieve 'objectivity', to carry the light of reason to every social problem. They wished to overcome prejudice. One prejudice, however, they did not consider. When they mentioned women at all, it was only to argue why women were and should be subordinate. Rousseau fed his ideal fictional woman only milk and sweets and made her a child, a doll, even as he offered a plan for a rich and complex education for his ideal fictional man. The *philosophes* spoke of human rights: but women were not included in the term *human* (French 1985, p. 183).

For women, this was an *age of exclusion* —from science and education, indeed from all institutions of learning, from all positions of influence, and from all decision-making roles.

## The age of anxiety, or the age of opportunity

The 19th century saw the beginning of existentialism with its emphasis on basic anxiety as that experience which constitutes human existence. Soren Kierkegaard wrote about the concept of Dread. Rollo May contends that W.H. Auden's poem 'The Age of Anxiety' (1947) is an accurate expression of the loneliness, alienation and meaninglessness commonly felt by people in this modern era.

. . . this stupid world where
Gadgets are gods and we go on talking,
. . . but remain alone,
Alive but alone, belonging—Where?—
Unattached as tumbleweed (May 1950, p. 44).

Also, Auden highlights the feelings of invisibility and redundancy that strike people at their very core:

It is getting late.
Shall we ever be asked for? Are we simply
    Not wanted at all? (May 1950, p. 38).

Existentialists such as Heidegger, Sartre, May and Tillich all refer to the lostness, the alienation people experience right down in the depths of their being, and it is this experience which prompts May to call this present period in history the age of anxiety.

There are various reasons given for the deep anxiety that pervades people's lives at this time—the increasing emphasis on materialism which leaves people spiritually empty; the psychologically devastating effects of war passed on from generation to generation; exposure through the mass media to world problems over which individuals feel they have no control and which consequently leave people with a general feeling of helplessness; the knowledge that, with nuclear arms, the destruction of the whole earth is now a very real possibility and the despair that comes with that knowledge; the emphasis on extreme individualism which insists that everyone is responsible for their own happiness, and the loneliness and isolation such an emphasis brings.

While existentialists refer to our recent history (19th and 20th centuries) as the age of anxiety, it is important to remember that others see it quite differently. Terms like the nuclear age, the technological age, the age of the computer, the age of opportunity are used with great optimism by many who believe life is better now than it has ever been at any other time in history.

Whatever the diagnosis about the age in which we live, the important thing for women to remember is that any analysis of society or the human condition (except those undertaken by feminists) is always done, consciously or unconsciously, with reference to men and not to women. The condition of men is what constitutes the human condition, and whatever is happening in women's lives at any given time in history is not recorded, precisely because it is not noticed. Thankfully feminist historians are changing this, even though many are still having to fight hard to have what they discover and write about women accepted as a legitimate account of history.

The question we must ask about this present period in history is: What has it been like for women?

## The ages of woman

The following is a description, in psychological terms, of the stages women can be said to have progressed through from the middle of the 19th century till now:

### The age of emptiness

The Industrial Revolution, while hailed as a period of great progress, nevertheless had the effect of depriving men of the feeling of control they were accustomed to. In order to maintain a sense of 'manhood', 19th century men degraded women even more than they had in the past. They

> . . . adopted an image, still popular today, of hardheaded hardheartedness, of harshness and brutality, toughness, *realism*.
>
> Women were cast into the roles that most contrasted with this one. They were 'exalted' as pure, virginal, frail maidens out of touch with reality and unable to bear its pressures; they needed men to intervene between them and the world, men to guide and control them . . . the fragile girl was the link between a man and something divinely pure, free from the taint of this new, dirty, completely male reality. The maidens grew up (or didn't) to be housewives who might still be exalted in literature and in their men's boasts, as angels, madonnas, sweet smiling agents of morality and divinity, but

who were also treated with peremptory contempt and authoritarian cruelty by men who required inferiors (French 1985, p. 202).

While 'masculine' qualities of aggressiveness, competitiveness, power and acquisitiveness were fostered and valued during the Industrial Revolution, 'feminine' qualities were further downgraded, so much so that 'men who demonstrated compassion, sensitivity, or indifference to acquisitiveness were deemed unfit' (French 1985, p. 203).

In both England and America, women from the emerging middle class were forced into the role of the keepers of morality and placed on a pedestal from which 'exalted' position they were denied involvement in the important affairs of the new industrialised, masculinised society. For women, life was constricted and empty:

> . . . women, constricted within an image of sweetness and docility, complaisance and gentleness, chastity and even nonsexuality, could maintain such qualities only by willfully blinding themselves to what was occurring in the outer world. Women who knew their own misery and resentment maintained brittle smiles, uttering pious phrases that masked rage and resentment; many fell ill—women's health was generally poor in nineteenth-century America (French 1985, pp. 203–4).

In Australia, in early 19th century colonial days, the role of women was well and truly planned out for them. In Anne Summers' words, women were forced into the roles of either 'damned whores' or 'God's police'. In the new colony, single immigrant women who were unable to find employment had no alternative but to sleep in the streets, completely vulnerable, preyed upon by men, treated as whores. When Carolyn Chisholm arrived in Sydney with her husband in the late 1830s, she

> . . . was horrified to discover the plight of the single women immigrants. She went round the streets and parks of Sydney, gathering up distressed women and took them into her home, but she soon recognized that large scale measures were necessary to alleviate the plight of what she estimated to be

six hundred women . . . She began by pressuring Governor
Gipps who grudgingly gave her the use of a building where,
on 26 October 1841, she opened a Female Immigrants Home
(Summers 1975, p. 300).

Carolyn Chisholm's immediate aim, after providing these
women with a place to live, was to find suitable employment for
them. Her ultimate aim, however, was for them to become wives
and mothers.

Chisholm had strong views on the contribution respectable
married women could make to a restructuring of Australian
society . . . She considered women to be 'God's Police', a
civilizing and moderating influence in an intemperate social
environment . . . She thought that even wild colonial Australia
would be elevated if men could be rescued from their
'enforced bachelorism' . . . (Summers 1975, pp. 301–2).

In the same way as single women were 'used' as whores, married
women were 'used' as moral police whose task it was to civilise
the men and make Australian society more respectable.

Though the situation for pioneer women in the harsh Australian bush was very different from that of women in England and
America, the psychological effect was similar. For Australian
women, too, it was a time of constriction, isolation and
emptiness.

### The age of involvement

In Europe, the United States and Australia, from the middle of
the 19th century, the campaign for women's suffrage was waged.
Women were denied the vote on the basis that they did not
understand politics and therefore the affairs of the nation were
best left to men. Also, women generally were denied employment, and those who were able to gain employment were denied
equal pay for equal work.

World War I changed everything for women in Europe and
the United States. With so many men occupied in the war,
women were welcomed into the labour market:

. . . they worked in blast furnaces, foundries, and plants
manufacturing steel plate, high explosives, armaments,

machine tools, agricultural implements, electrical, railway, automobile, and airplane parts. They also worked in the smelting and refining of brass and copper, in the refining of oil, and in the production of chemicals, fertilizers, and leather goods. Gone were their frailty, their incompetence, their mental weakness; above all, gone was their position of competition with men (French 1985, p. 215).

Australian women were not needed in the labour market as much as their overseas sisters. 'Instead, the Great War—as it came ironically to be called—had the effect of cementing and consolidating the notion that women's main social function was to bear children and to influence those around them into dutiful civic submission' (Summers 1975, p. 380).

Australian women became involved in great numbers in pro-war and anti-war campaigns. Motherhood gave their involvement in such campaigns legitimacy and they fought with vigour and assertiveness. The pro-war women, as God's Police, saw it as their duty to urge their sons and other men to enlist, and also to support the war effort in every possible way. Anti-war women, with equal vigour, arranged rallies and other forms of action, calling on people to desist from participating. The war provided women with an excuse to become involved in ways that had never been open to them before.

World War II also provided women with opportunities for involvement. This time Australian women were coopted by the labour market in the same way as women of other countries. Federal governments suddenly provided funding for child care centres and arranged special training programs 'to teach women skills which, a few months earlier, they had been considered incapable of learning. Women instantly assumed positions of responsibility and authority . . .' (French 1985, p. 226) when it suited men to have them involved.

While both world wars brought much worry and sadness for women—never knowing if their husbands or sons would return from overseas, and if they did, in what state they would return—at the same time, there was a positive side to the situation. In the absence of men, women were free to do some of the jobs they always knew they could handle if given the opportunity. Women proved to themselves and to men and governments that they were capable of much more than the narrow roles of wife and mother ascribed to them—by a society determined to keep the power in the hands of men by denying women control at every level. Both world wars proved to be an age of involvement for women.

## The age of isolation

When each war was over, however, it was a different story. Just as women were forced into involvement to keep their countries running while men were away at war, so women were forced out of involvement when the men returned.

Australian women had won the right to vote before World War I, but the battle was not won in other countries till after the war. British women finally won the vote in 1918 and American women in 1920. After suffrage was achieved the prevailing attitude in Europe and the United States was that the fight for women's rights was over. Women had won the battle and should now be satisfied to go back to the domestic arena and support their husbands in rebuilding society after the trauma of the war. Jobs were taken from women and given back to men. Women were encouraged to have children and pour all their energy into making home a place where husband and children would receive all the nurturing they required.

Being forced once more into the isolation of the home after having had a taste of real involvement, many women were left with a sense of numbness. They had thought there was going to be more to their lives after the war and after the vote, but instead they seemed to be facing stronger opposition than ever. 'Discrimination against women hardened and was fixed into policy' (French 1985, p. 225). Women were excluded in great numbers from universities, medical schools, law schools, industry and commerce.

Then came the depression of the 1930s, which made it even worse for women. 'During the Depression, laws were passed denying employment to married women; women were fired before men. The jobs still open to women were mainly the very lowest paid, jobs men would not take' (French 1985, p. 226).

As mentioned above, the situation for women changed dramatically with the onset of World War II, but as soon as the war ended

> . . . the prewar status quo promptly reasserted itself. Men were reinstated in their jobs and granted the benefits of the GI Bill; women were fired, the child-care centres dismantled, and the training programs ended. Some women managed to remain in the labor force, but at lower rank. The old cult of domesticity also reappeared . . . (French 1985, p. 226).

The cult of domesticity was a manifestation of the needs of women and men after the harrowing experience of the war. Both 'men and women involved in World War II ended sick at heart, exhausted and disgusted with mass murder, with the terrible machines of war, with killing, deprivation, and sacrifice. They craved peaceful order, pleasure, affection; they needed to create new life after the devastation' (French 1985, p. 497).

The problem with the new cult of domesticity was that it convinced whole nations of people that the peace and happiness they were looking for could be found in 'love, marriage, children, and a home' (French 1985, p. 497). Such a belief

> . . . locked women firmly into the domestic realm by making them responsible for the creation and physical maintenance of this [peace and happiness] . . . thus they would not protest their renewed exclusion from the workplace; and it locked men firmly into their work, necessary for the economic maintenance of this [peace and happiness] . . . (French 1985, p. 497).

For women, the situation in Australia after World War II was exactly the same as in Europe and the United States.

> Whether they wanted to or not, they were expected to return . . . to the pre-war division of labour and status and power. Those women who tried to retain their war-time jobs, or to use the skills they had acquired in some related job, were expected to make way for returning ex-servicemen. A group of women in Melbourne who had been transport drivers during the war applied to the Melbourne City Council for licences to drive taxis but were refused on the grounds that all jobs were

being made available to men who had served. What women had done was not considered to be comparable. Many protested at being shunted back to the home . . . But most women were as quiescent as they had always been. They were used to carrying out orders, to acting as deputies, and now that a new directive had come through, one that said 'populate or our nation will perish', most women obediently went back home and started having a baby (Summers 1975, pp. 419–20).

The period between the wars and the two decades following World War II constituted periods of severe isolation for women in western countries. During the 1950s and 1960s, women who during the war 'had begun to expand their self-definition and to realize that they had capabilities beyond those of mother and housewife' (Summers 1975, p. 425) nevertheless obediently retreated to the home and tried to make the best of it. Betty Friedan speaks of the 'propaganda campaign' waged for more than fifteen years 'to give women "prestige" as housewives' (Friedan 1963, p. 223). The result was the condition that has come to be known as 'suburban neurosis'.

The problem lay buried, unspoken for many years in the minds of American women. It was a strange stirring, a sense of dissatisfaction, a yearning that women suffered in the middle of the twentieth century in the United States. Each suburban wife struggled with it alone. As she made the beds, shopped for groceries, matched slipcover material, ate peanut butter sandwiches with her children, chauffered Cub Scouts and Brownies, lay beside her husband at night, she was afraid to ask even of herself the silent question: 'Is this all?' (Friedan 1963, p. 13).

Women made endless visits to doctors and psychiatrists but were unable to put into words what was really going on for them. Doctors were puzzled. All they knew was that the number of women coming to them with the same symptoms was escalating. They called it variously, 'the housewife's syndrome', 'the housewife's blight', 'housewife's fatigue', 'suburban neurosis', and so on. Betty Friedan called it 'the problem that has no name' (Friedan 1963, pp. 13–29), a problem that she had sensed herself when she was a suburban housewife bringing up three children. Early in the 1960s, as a reporter, she started interviewing women about this problem that has no name.

> Sometimes a woman would say 'I feel empty somehow . . . incomplete.' Or she would say, 'I feel as if I don't exist'. Sometimes she blotted out the feeling with a tranquillizer. Sometimes she thought the problem was with her husband, or her children, or that what she really needed was to redecorate her house, or move to a better neighbourhood, or have an affair, or another baby. Sometimes, she went to a doctor with symptoms she could hardly describe: 'A tired feeling . . . I get so angry with the children it scares me . . . I feel like crying without any reason' (Friedan 1963, p. 18).

## The age of awareness

Slowly women began talking to each other about this problem that has no name. Each woman in her own suburban prison, isolated from the world outside the home, thought that she must be the only woman in the world to experience such dissatisfaction, such despair. Now she was talking to other women, not just about children, husband, home, the safe topics, but *real* talk—about loneliness, isolation, emptiness, depression, disillusionment, the fear of going crazy—and she felt amazing relief to know she was not alone. Countless numbers of women began expressing exactly the same feelings.

All over the United States, Great Britain, Europe and Australia, small groups of women began meeting in each other's homes regularly, in what became known as Consciousness Raising (CR) groups. Dale Spender refers to 'the revolutionary nature of CR' (Spender 1980, p. 108). Women were not supposed to talk to each other, and when they did, they were not supposed to take each other's talk seriously. The talk that took place in CR groups was taken very seriously indeed, and 'the males who objected to—who were even frightened by—this radical change had good grounds for their anxiety. They were justified in thinking woman talk was dangerous and a threat to their existence' (Spender 1980, p. 108).

For women, the age of awareness had dawned. The more they

talked, the more their awareness grew—awareness of the cleverly orchestrated propaganda that had conned them into remaining isolated in their homes for so long; awareness of the oppression of women in patriarchal society; awareness of the extent of male violence against women and children; awareness that the boredom, emptiness and indifference they felt in their relationships with their partners were not uncommon feelings amongst women. 'It was not *they* who were at fault after all, but the men who organized and controlled their lives' (Coote and Campbell 1982, p. 14).

For most women courageous enough to become involved in CR groups, the experience was exhilarating. Coote and Campbell speak of 'the moment of recognition, the sudden, excited discovery of . . . of what exactly? Of themselves, of the value of women and the pure pleasure of their company, of a new sense of identification and a new intimation of power' (Coote and Campbell 1982, p. 25).

### The age of anger

As well as being exhilarating and life-affirming, this period was also frightening for most of the women involved in their own consciousness-raising because their new awareness brought with it a welling-up of anger, the like of which they had never before allowed themselves to feel. Years and years of repressed anger came rushing to the surface and began finding expression. There was anger at the realisation that, for thousands of years, women had been conned into believing that male control was somehow part of the 'natural' order of things, and anger also at the realisation that male control, in fact, existed only because men in every generation worked hard to ensure that women and women's intelligence, talents, energy, confidence, potential were suppressed.

Women began doing research from their own perspective rather than the mandatory male perspective. In every field of study, women were asking 'difficult' questions and uncovering answers that caused women everywhere to be angry. Some were angry at men and oppressive male institutions, while others were angry at the women who were angry at men. Many women just did not want to hear the answers to the questions that were being asked, because open acknowledgement of the deliberate oppression of women by men could unleash in them years of repressed anger, a reaction which many preferred to avoid.

The following are examples of the kinds of questions being asked by those women who wanted to know the truth, and the answers they discovered:

*Question:* Why are there so few women in positions of authority in the public service, politics, the business sector, the church, etc.?

*Answer:* Because the success structures of society are made for men, and women are actively discouraged from entering courses of study or paths of employment that may lead to such positions of authority.

*Question:* Why is God portrayed always as a male God?

*Answer:* Because it was men who decided what God was like, and it was men who proceeded, through theology and religious institutions, to indoctrinate everyone else.

Merlin Stone uncovered some very interesting facts about the importance of Goddess worship in early times. 'In prehistoric and early historic periods of human development, religions existed in which people revered their supreme creator as female. The Great Goddess—the Divine Ancestress—had been worshipped from the beginnings of the Neolithic periods of 7000 BC until the closing of the last Goddess temples, about AD 500' (Stone 1976, p. 2).

She discovered also that the Judaeo-Christian religions deliberately and systematically suppressed Goddess worship and insisted on the worship of the male God, Jehovah. 'Archaeological, mythological and historical evidence all reveal that the female religion, far from naturally fading away, was the victim of centuries of continual persecution and suppression by the advocates of the newer religions which held male deities as supreme' (Stone 1976, p. 3). These newer, male-dominated religions also came up with the story of Adam and Eve, the creation myth which was designed to make us believe 'it was decreed by God that woman must submit to the dominance of man—who was at that time divinely presented with the right to rule over her—from that moment until now' (Stone 1976, p. 2).

*Question:* Why does the law seem to discriminate against women?

*Answer:* Because the law was designed by men with men in mind.

*Question:* Why is the extent of male violence against women hidden in our society? Why is our society not incensed at the undeniable evidence of violence against women and children in the home? Why are 'decent' men not outraged in the face of so much evidence of the sexual abuse of children by their fathers and other so-called 'protectors'? Why are 'decent' men so silent about the rape (including gang-rape) of women by men?

*Answer:* Because it could be, as Susan Brownmiller suggests, that all men benefit from the existence of rape in society.

Although many men are appalled at the thought of their partners or daughters being raped, Brownmiller suggests that, at some level, it does not suit men to eradicate rape from society because it serves to keep 'all women in a thrall of anxiety and fear. Rape is to women . . . the ultimate physical threat by which all men keep all women in a state of psychological intimidation' (1975, p. 281). The same could be said about all forms of male violence against women and girls. Its very existence is enough to keep women under control. 'Decent' men can go on being 'decent', secure in the knowledge that their position of power over women will be maintained.

*Question:* Why do governments pour so much more money into defence than they do into welfare services?

*Answer:* Because war is what men do, and most welfare recipients are women.

Women were angry, also, at the realisation that they were just as oppressed in their personal relationships with men as they were in the wider society. Most women, when they marry, have an expectation that theirs will be a relationship between two adults, and that both adults will endeavour to interact with maturity, cooperation and sensitivity to each other's needs. Even when all the evidence around them suggests the majority of relationships fail to achieve that, most women somehow manage to convince themselves that 'ours will be different'.

Early in the 1970s, when women in great numbers began allowing themselves to look honestly at their relationships with male partners, most had to admit that their relationship was no different from all the others, and they began to be angry. The kinds of things they were angry about then are the same things women are angry about today. Often, one hears the following comments from women:

• *He lives like a single man, with no consideration for anyone but himself.* Many men, even after they marry and have children, continue to live as they did when they were single—going out whenever they like, spending a lot of time with their mates, drinking a lot, spending money whenever they feel like it, and so on. They seem to have no concept of sharing and make no attempt at cooperative living. Their idea of a happy marriage seems to be: 'I do what I want to do, and you fit in with me and my job, my decisions, my needs, my desires'.

• *He's no different from the children.* Many women testify to the fact that they feel like they are married to a child who wants his own way all the time, throws tantrums, sulks, jokes around, teases, and insists on instant gratification. Whenever he wants something, he wants it *now*, with little consideration for the needs or wants of others.

• *He refuses to communicate effectively within the relationship.* The experience of many women is that whenever they try to communicate with their male partners about serious matters, particularly if it involves an expression of dissatisfaction or unhappiness, they come up against a brick wall. Instead of listening, instead of displaying a genuine concern about what is being expressed, instead of wanting to talk it through till it is resolved to the satisfaction of both partners, most men respond with silence, or ignore, or withdrawal, or ridicule, or anger, or violence.

• *He goes to great lengths to ensure that he maintains control.* Many women say that standing up for their rights in a relationship is not worth the hassle, because men are not interested in equality and fair play. They are only interested in winning. The kinds of methods men employ to ensure that they stay in control include: refusing to work cooperatively, refusing to consider a compromise; threats of violence, threats about walking out on the relationship and finding someone else, threats of suicide, threats of murder-suicide; moodiness, emotional withdrawal for days or weeks or even months; revenge in a variety of ways. Research undertaken by Sally Cline and Dale Spender reveals that 'women who refuse to please or placate men rarely get away with it' (Cline and Spender 1987, p. 169). In chapter 8 of their book they discuss some of the sanctions men employ in order to get revenge, ranging from embarrassing anti-social behaviour (loud yawning, belching, spitting, passing gas), to violence, rape, intimidation of partners, and sexual abuse of daughters (Cline and Spender 1987, pp. 169–91).

When a woman's consciousness is raised to the fact that her partner's unacceptable behaviour is part of his scheme to maintain control, she begins to understand why she has felt so powerless for so long in her relationship, and her anger rises to the surface and begins to explode. From that moment on, her anger allows her to experience a new kind of empowerment.

## The age of expectation

Even though women's new awareness in the late 1960s and into the 1970s was accompanied by so much anger, it was also an age of expectation. Women actually believed they were creating a new society where the attitudes of women and men toward each other would change, where relationships would reflect the greater desire of women and men to understand each other, and where there would be equality of respect and sensitivity. Many spoke of the women's liberation movement as that movement which would bring about human liberation—liberation for men as well as women.

How naive we were to believe that men also wanted to work toward such high ideals! What we have seen is that while women have been working to improve themselves, to enhance their interpersonal skills, to make their relationships with men

71

more equal and therefore more satisfying, and to improve their status in society, men have not responded as women had hoped. Rather, men have responded with ignore, or ridicule, or defensiveness, or manipulation, or anger, or violence, all designed to discourage women's efforts at equality and bring about a return to what some men might call the 'good old days' when they had total control and women accepted their lot in life and made the best of it.

When the United Nations declared 1975 as International Women's Year and many countries of the world responded by giving special attention to the needs and status of women, women's expectations were high. Things appeared to be changing and were, in fact, changing. Women's research and writing, women speaking out about injustices, women working within the system as well as agitating outside the system, pushing for change at every level, all of these activities seemed to be having a positive effect. So powerful was the feminist revolution at that time that the whole of society was changing and everybody knew things would never be quite the same again. Even those women and men who refused to take the women's movement seriously did not escape its effect.

In Australia, feminists who had worked so hard and who were suffering a fair degree of burn-out could nevertheless see some of the fruits of their labour. There were new government initiatives designed to improve the status of women, Anti-discrimination legislation, legislation for Equal Employment Opportunity, Women's Advisory groups at federal and state levels, funding for women's refuges and rape crisis centres. There was much needed law reform, including the Family Law Act and rape law reform.

At a personal level, too, women in great numbers were moving out of the isolation of their homes and talking to each other, taking courses in Assertiveness Training, going to college and university, entering the workplace. Much progress was evident—but something was still not right.

## The age of anxiety

During the last ten years or so (since early in the 1980s), while women's awareness and anger have continued to grow, our expectation of a truly changed society has waned. Part of women's experience now is that while ostensibly we have gained much, in reality nothing seems to have changed substantially except that the discrimination that once was obvious now occurs in more covert ways. While certain laws have made it more difficult for men to discriminate openly against women, the basic male attitude toward women does not appear to have changed. There is still evidence of a fundamental lack of respect on the part of men for women and women's capabilities. Some go so far as to say that the continuing level of male violence against women and girls—criminal assault, rape, incest, pornography, sexual harrassment, murder (all of which go largely unchecked and unpunished)—indicates not simply a lack of respect, but a fundamental hatred of women by men (Forward 1987).

The expectation and superficial appearance of change brought about by the Women's Movement, combined with the contradictory day-to-day experience of women that nothing seems really to have changed, sets up a situation in which anxiety is the only appropriate response; hence, the naming of the period from the early 1980s till now as the age of anxiety for women.

Remembering that anxiety occurs in response to things that happen at a deeper than conscious level, it will be seen that it is not women's awareness or anger or fighting against injustices that causes anxiety, but an unconscious, nagging, empty feeling that, even after all they have been through and achieved, something is still not right. If women knew in their conscious minds what was wrong the appropriate emotion might be anger or disappointment or depression, but when all they have to go on is an unconscious, awful feeling that there are still strong forces working against them, the emotion they experience is anxiety.

Admittedly, when women's experience is described in this way it sounds very much like paranoia, but the reality is that, while concessions have been made, many forces still work against women achieving equal status with men. The only difference is that whereas once those forces were blatant, they are now more subtle and insidious. We now turn to an examination of these forces—first at a societal level, then at an interpersonal level, and finally at a personal level.

Focusing first on society at large, it must be said that this is a time when everything appears to be going well for women in terms of educational and employment opportunities, but women's experience is that *something is still radically wrong.*

Because of the women's movement and its effect on society as a whole, women are encouraged now to have greater expectations of themselves. This era is an era of equal opportunities for women and men, we are told. It is even (falsely) referred to as the post-feminist era, intimating that the battle for women's rights has been fought and won, that discrimination against women is a thing of the past, and that any criticism of, or anger at, the way things are done now is therefore inappropriate. Exactly the same attitude arose after women won the vote early this century.

> With these gains won, the women's movement was proclaimed victorious—and over. Further agitation was declared unnecessary, and male politicians and businessmen were no longer willing to listen to women's demands. Even the sensitive British novelist E. M. Forster could not understand why Virginia Woolf—a friend of his—had written *Three Guineas* in 1938; in *Two Cheers for Democracy* he called Woolf's great and gracious essay 'cantankerous'; he could not understand why she was fussing about such an 'old-fashioned' thing as feminism when everyone knew the battle was over and women had won it (French 1985, p. 225).

The emphasis today, as then, is supposed to be on the positive. There are opportunities for women, we are told, and all women need to do is have the confidence to take hold of those opportunities. Women have done that, women do have greater expectations, and they find that everything *is* available to them—but not quite!

In education, for example, there is no barrier to women entering university provided they meet all the male requirements for tertiary study. There is no barrier to women achieving higher degrees and moving right on up to the top of their field, provided they are prepared to do their research and writing according to male definitions of what constitutes 'acceptable' scientific research. In most of the faculties at most universities, the 'experts' in any field are still seen to be male (as evidenced by reading lists consisting almost solely of male authors and ignoring the contribution of women writers in the field). Feminist theory, developed and refined over twenty years, is still not accepted in most institutions of higher learning as legitimate academic theory. Education is available to women, but only if women are prepared to do it on male terms. In other words, education is available to women—but not quite.

In employment, women are encouraged to take their place alongside men in the workplace, but while women's employment opportunities have improved, it is often the case that opportunities are denied them for reasons that seem quite inadequate.

Following the running of the 1990 Melbourne Cup, a television program focused on a jockey who had not been able to get a ride in the prestigious Melbourne Cup event. The jockey was a young woman who had been very successful in her home state of Tasmania. A year or so before the 1990 Cup she had moved to Melbourne to advance her career only to find that nobody would employ her. The most revealing part of the television program was the snippets of interviews with trainers and other jockeys who were asked if she should be given the same chance as male jockeys. Most of them said the track was no place for a woman, but no valid reasons were given. Several of them said a woman did not have the strength required to handle a race horse (rather amusing coming from some of the smallest men in the country!). One can only assume that horses in Tasmania are different from those on the mainland, since the young woman had won so many races in Tasmania over fields of male jockeys.

While similar stories could be told in many areas of employment, it must be conceded that some women do achieve positions worthy of their expertise in both the public service and the private sector, but again their experience is that they have achieved something—but not quite.

Many women in positions of considerable authority speak of the experience of feeling invisible. Giving one's opinion or analysis of a situation in a staff meeting and having it totally ignored is a common experience of women who appear to the outside world to have 'made it'. Their feeling of invisibility is compounded when, twenty minutes later, they hear that same opinion articulated by a male in the group, only to find it taken up as an important contribution to the discussion. In these situations, aware women have observed that most of the eye contact in such forums occurs between the men. When a woman begins to speak, the male eyes are often busily occupied scanning the papers in front of them, looking at their watches, or gazing out the window. The attitude of male superiors is often experienced by women as dismissive or impatient or patronising, in sharp contrast to the supportive, patient, encouraging attitude they display toward other men.

Most women do try to believe that things are different these days and that they have nothing to complain about. When a woman is treated with ignore, made to feel invisible, passed over for no good reason, she often ends up blaming herself because there seems nobody else to blame. The resultant feelings of inadequacy, emptiness, invisibility and confusion are all feelings which breed anxiety.

Turning attention now to the interpersonal sphere, this is a time when women want to believe their personal relationships with men are changing, but day-to-day experience suggests that *it might only be women who have changed.*

As a result of feminist input into how relationships ought to be, many women now talk to their partners about the qualities of a good relationship. They talk about equality, about the sharing of responsibilities for housework, cooking, the care of the children, about the need for both partners to have the satisfaction of working outside the home and contributing financially to the family's welfare, and so on. In her enthusiasm a woman either fails to notice, or makes some excuse for, the fact that it is usually she who initiates such discussions and she who brings energy to the discussion and ideas for improvement of the partnership. Any thoughts she may have about his seeming lack of interest are usually put out of her mind in her desire to believe she has a close-to-perfect relationship.

Many women do believe it ought to be possible for both partners to have a full-time job outside the home and share home duties and care of the children, but the experience of most women in that situation seems to be that primary responsibility for home and children is still left squarely on their shoulders.

Over the last decade or so the 'superwoman' syndrome has seen a glorification of a woman's ability to hold down at least two full-time jobs, one being that of wife, mother, housekeeper and all that goes with those roles (more than a full-time job in terms of hours and energy expended), and the other being her full-time paid employment. The superwoman label, while purporting to praise women for all they are able to achieve, in fact covers up the truth that a woman only has to be a superwoman because she gets little or no help from her partner. (Single mothers in the paid workforce have always had to perform two full-time jobs, but the 'superwoman' label seems to be confined to women in full-time employment who are mothers *and* wives.) What the superwoman label ignores is that such women live extremely stressful lives and are physically and emotionally exhausted much of the time. The situation for such women is exacerbated by the knowledge that such stress cannot be borne indefinitely and that, as a consequence, failure is inevitable.

The other big area of concern for women in their relationships with men centres around communication. Women witness their partners communicating with other people in social situations, in work-related activities, on the sporting field, and cannot help wondering why their partner's ability and willingness to communicate does not extend to the home-front. Dale Spender drew attention to the fact that while men dominate conversations in social situations—by talking a lot, directing their comments to other men in the group, ignoring women's contributions to the discussion, feeling free to interrupt women whenever they want to, hijacking the conversation, changing the topic to suit their own interests, and so on—in personal, one-to-one situations with women, men's reluctance to communicate is obvious. Women expend an immense amount of energy, in one-to-one situations, trying to encourage their partners to communicate, but often to no avail.

The following, from Spender's research, is an example of a conversation in which the woman is 'making the effort, "drawing him out", until he chooses to take over and to "hold the floor"' (Spender 1980, p. 48).

Female: Did he have the papers ready for you?

Male: Mmm.

Female: And were they all right . . . was anything missing?

Male: Not that I could see.

Female: Well that must have been a relief, anyway . . .

Female: I suppose everything went well after that?

Male: Almost.

Female: Oh. Was there something else?

Male: Yes, actually.

Female: It wasn't X . . . was it? . . . He didn't let you down again?

Male: I'd say he did.

Female: He really is irresponsible, you know, you should get . . .

Male: I'm going to do something about it. It was just about the last straw today. How many times do you think that makes this week? . . .

'By my reckoning', Spender comments, 'the woman makes eight conversational gambits to which the man gives a perfunctory response. But he is tempted by the ninth, and he interrupts, and proceeds' (Spender 1980, p. 49).

There is a great deal of evidence to suggest women are not happy with the level of men's communication in relationships. Of the 4000 women interviewed in Shere Hite's most recent study, '98 per cent of (them) . . . say they would like more verbal closeness with the men they love; they want the men in their lives to talk more about their own personal thoughts, feelings, plans, and questions, and to ask them about theirs . . .' (Hite 1987, p. 5).

Is men's unwillingness to communicate with women due to their perception of intimate talk and expression of feelings as feminine and weak, Hite asks, or 'could there be an element of men unconsciously wanting to remind women to "know their place", to keep a certain distance appropriate between two non-equals? ... Is good communication a form of equality with women which many men are not yet ready to participate in?' (Hite 1987, p. 25).

Whatever the reason for men's refusal to communicate with women, the effect is that women are left wondering about many things. Much of a woman's energy is used up trying to guess what the man in her life is thinking and feeling, trying to find ways of getting him to open up, waiting for the 'right time' to broach a subject, believing that if only she can find the key, say the right words, then he will begin talking.

The anxiety of wondering what her partner is thinking or feeling leads a woman to look for excuses for his behaviour, so that her anxiety does not overwhelm her. The following are common excuses women invent:

- He really does care. He just doesn't know how to express it.

- He's always preoccupied with work. He's just got so much on his mind.

- He's a very deep person—very private—keeps everything to himself.

- I blame his mother. She never encouraged him to express himself when he was young.

- I blame myself. I'm obviously not approaching him properly.

Women desperately want to believe the excuses they hear coming from their own lips, but many are secretly afraid the truth might simply be that men are just not interested in open, honest, cooperative, equal relationships with women. Refusal to consider the plethora of evidence in support of this possibility, while secretly fearing it, causes women much anxiety.

Turning now to the personal level, it is apparent that anxiety exists as the context for women's lives not only because of what is happening at the social and interpersonal levels, but also because of women's own intrapersonal struggle. To put it simply, this is a time when *women are hiding their feelings from themselves.* The pressure on a woman to ignore her true feelings is coming both from outside and inside herself.

The outside pressures are those which exist in society as a reaction to what are called the 'excesses' of the Women's Movement. In an effort to get women to suppress their anger at men, the undeniably reasonable statement that 'men have a difficult time too', has become popular. Any reasonable woman will admit that men are also victims of their conditioning, but instead of insisting that men work to rid themselves of the effects of their conditioning, the onus has been placed on women to ease up on men. Such a plea for a 'balanced' attitude has resulted in women's anger being put away, allowing men (who usually operate out of an ethic of expediency) to relax and continue doing what they have always done.

Women are encouraged to be positive, constructive, to try to understand why men do the things they do, to support them, forgive them, help them, and share the blame with them. So, if your partner continually refuses to speak to you or listen to you or acknowledge that you are a human being, you are encouraged not to be angry at him for treating you like that but to feel sorry for him and to try to help him. If your partner is violent and continually assaults you physically and sexually, you are encouraged not to be angry with him for the pain and fear and indignity he has subjected you to, but to try to get him to agree to go with you to joint counselling, where you will look at what you are *both* doing wrong.

These days it is fashionable to speak of male violence in the home in terms of a 'violent relationship', and to deal with the so-called violent relationship by a process called mediation. The truth is that, nine times out of ten, it is not a violent relationship. Both partners are not violent. Rather, one partner (usually the male) is violent toward the other (usually the female). Mediation has the potential for moving the focus away from the man's responsibility to stop his own violent behaviour, and placing the responsibility for changing the violent behaviour on the shoulders of both partners. All therapists know that what will actually occur in therapy when the man is there under sufferance is that the woman will be there working hard to effect some changes in the relationship, and the man will simply be there.

Similarly, with regard to child sexual abuse, the fashionable thing these days is to talk about 'the abusing family', taking the focus off the unacceptable behaviour of the perpetrator and on to the family as a whole. What this effectively means is that the daughter who is the victim, and whose life has been scarred forever, is encouraged to share the blame with her father. The mother, too, is counselled to put away her anger and share the blame. Taking the blame off the perpetrator, however, only serves to relieve him of responsibility for the crime he has committed and leave the rest of the family with unexpressed and unresolved anger.

Many women respond with relief to the pressures coming from outside themselves to suppress their anger, because such a response matches the pressures coming from inside themselves. Anger is not an emotion women generally feel comfortable with, and whenever they are confronted with a situation that stirs up angry feelings, they immediately (often unconsciously) turn those feelings into something else. This process is, in fact, a defence against reality, which Freud referred to as 'repression through reaction formation' (Freud 1936, p. 30).

The following is an example of how the process occurs. A woman gives her opinion in a discussion involving her husband and several of their friends. Her husband tells her her opinion is ridiculous and goes on to give his enlightened opinion, which appears to be received enthusiastically by the group. She feels devastated, embarrassed, humiliated, isolated, and furiously angry at him for treating her with such disdain. Aware that her feelings of anger are almost impossible to contain, she becomes anxious. She tells herself she is being childish. He surely did not mean to hurt her, she reminds herself. As a matter of fact, she remembers several years ago when he actually said he would not want to hurt her for the world. She represses her anger and turns it into self-recrimination and guilt. How could she have been so unkind? She ought to be grateful that she has such a good husband. She then overcompensates for her 'unkind' thoughts by being over-caring, over-concerned, over-attentive toward him, and overwhelmed by her love for him.

While the process involved in reaction formation allows a woman to lower her anxiety level momentarily by denying her true feelings, it actually contributes to a much more serious and debilitating anxiety. To accept blame when one knows one is not to blame, to smile when one wants to cry, to be kind and caring when one is filled with anger, is not only dishonest in the extreme, but also causes the kind of self-alienation that can result in deep and severe anxiety. Consequently, women must stop pretending things are not as they are, and make a determined effort to make their real feelings known to themselves. To be prepared to acknowledge one's own anger is the first step toward finding the courage to express that anger and insist that changes be made.

The above description, in psychological terms, of the last two centuries of women's experiences, helps us to see the path that has led women to this present time in history when we seem almost to be trapped in an age of anxiety. In order to be released from the anxiety of the present time, perhaps women have no alternative but to find the courage to move forward into another age of anger, and this time, to maintain our anger until all male violence against women ceases, all sexual abuse of children ceases, all treatment of women as inferior beings ceases, and until women enjoy the same right as men to be fully in control of our own lives.

# 3

# Women's powerlessness as cause

THE focus of attention will move, at this point, from women's *collective* experience of anxiety to the experience of *individual* women who are anxiety-sufferers, keeping in mind the fact that women's collective experience of powerlessness, invisibility and emotional deprivation, referred to in the previous chapter as the 'age of anxiety for women', provides a background against which individual women can gain a clearer understanding of how their own condition developed.

## Why me?

The fact that anxiety is said to be the context in which all women live, but that only some women develop severe anxiety and panic conditions, will naturally prompt anxiety-sufferers to ask: Why me? If oppression is the experience of all women, why is it that only *some* women develop anxiety as a serious psychological problem? The answer to that question is that *only those women who are predisposed to severe anxiety* will actually develop it when they are confronted with experiences of women's oppression. Those who do not have the preconditions for anxiety will respond in other ways, such as depression, addiction, eating disorders—or anger, which is actually the most healthy response to oppression.

## What are the preconditions?

What are the conditions already present in some women's lives from childhood or adolescence that are likely to lead to the development of anxiety? The need to address this question leads us to embark on an exploration of three important schools of psychological thought with a view to discovering some of the theories about cause. It must be stated that there is no intention here to do an exhaustive study of all theories presented by all schools of thought. Rather, each of the three theories included has been chosen because of its ability to highlight the role of powerlessness or invisibility or emotional deprivation in the development of severe anxiety conditions.

This chapter will discuss some of the psychoanalytic theories with their strong emphasis on *powerlessness* in childhood as the major precondition for the development of severe anxiety. Chapter 4 focuses on existential psychotherapeutic theory and emphasises the experience of *invisibility* as a major precondition, while chapter 5 presents feminist psychotherapeutic theory and focuses on *emotional deprivation* as a major precondition.

## The search for a cause

Only two facts are known for sure about cause. The first is that there is not one simple cause that applies to everybody. If there were, then the treatment of severe anxiety would be made so much easier. It is the fact that the cause is difficult to identify with any degree of certainty that makes the condition so puzzling for sufferer and therapist alike. The second fact that is known for sure is that the cause of each woman's anxiety is to be found within that individual woman. For that reason, if you are an anxiety-sufferer and you want to know about the origins of your condition, you must be prepared to engage in your own individual search for possible causes by uncovering as much as you can of the interpersonal dynamics that existed in your childhood, and also the feelings related to those dynamics which you repressed. This can be done alone, or with the help of a therapist who is sensitive to the particular needs and fears of anxiety-sufferers.

## *Warning: To search for a cause can be counterproductive*

It is important to reiterate here a point which was made in chapter 1: *that finding the cause of your condition is not a prerequisite to effecting a cure.* As a matter of fact, for someone who has not learned the kind of treatment procedure outlined in chapter 6, a preoccupation with cause usually makes the condition worse. Anyone who is at present in the grip of anxiety attacks is well advised to stop worrying about what causes them and focus all her attention on getting the treatment process right first. There will be plenty of time later to come back and explore the question of cause.

For those who are ready to enquire about cause, it needs to be understood that not all the theories you read about in these three chapters will 'fit' you. The important thing is that you think carefully about each of them and take from them anything that might help in the development of your own personal theory about the cause of your own condition.

## Psychoanalytic theories

Beginning with Freud, psychoanalysis has contributed greatly to the study of anxiety. The most thought-provoking contributions for the purposes of this study are the work of Freud, Rank, Adler and Horney.

### *Sigmund Freud (Austria, 1856–1939)*

Throughout his career, Freud presented three different theories about the cause of what he called 'neurotic' anxiety. It seems that as he had more and more exposure to anxiety over the years, through his work with patients, his thinking about the condition kept changing.

His first theory, stated very briefly, was that *repression causes anxiety.* This idea arose out of his belief that, during the so-called phallic stage of development (ages four to five) when the focus of a child's attention is the sex organs, every boy is in love with his mother and sees his father as a rival and a threat, and every girl is in love with her father and sees her mother as a rival and a threat. Because of this situation, both boys and girls at this very young age have strong conflicting feelings of love and aggressiveness, both of which they are afraid to express because of their perception that to do so would result in losing the love of one or both parents. Consequently they repress their feelings, and it is this repression of love and aggressiveness, Freud believed, that is transformed into anxiety.

His second theory is, in fact, the opposite of the first, a fact which he was quite willing to admit. After a period of observation with a young patient, he came to the conclusion that *anxiety causes repression.*

> We should have expected to find that it was a libidinal cathexis of the boy's mother as object which, as a result of repression, had been changed into anxiety . . . I cannot present you with the detailed steps of an investigation such as this; it will be enough to say that the surprising result was the opposite of what we expected. It was not the repression that created the anxiety; the anxiety was there earlier; it was the anxiety that made the repression (Freud 1964, p. 118).

The obvious question arising from this hypothesis is: Where does this earlier anxiety come from? Freud's answer to that question is that it comes from a basic fear of separation caused by the trauma of birth. The act of birth itself, he says, is extremely traumatic because of the experience of physical separation from the mother. Later, as the child begins to relate to the mother and father, anxiety about separation is intensified because of the child's love for one parent and aggressiveness toward the other. Boys fear castration at the hands of their father as punishment for loving their mother, and girls fear the loss of their mother's love as punishment for loving their father. In his later writing, Freud seems to drop his castration anxiety theory, and refers to the anxiety of both boys and girls in terms of fear of loss of parental love.

Up to this point, Freud is actually talking about normal anxiety. It only becomes neurotic anxiety, he says, in those people who '. . . are unable to surmount the fear of loss of love; [those who] never become sufficiently independent of other people's love' (Freud 1964, p. 121).

86

Freud's third and final theory is that *neurotic anxiety occurs when a person's normal signalling fails.* This theory seems to be an attempt to explain the mechanics of normal and neurotic anxiety, and as such is a continuation of his second theory. He talks about signal anxiety and primary anxiety. When a person is confronted by a situation of impending trauma, he says, the ego normally signals that there is danger, and the person responds by fleeing or protecting herself in some other way. Signal anxiety is normal anxiety. Primary anxiety, on the other hand, occurs when the ego is powerless to protect itself from 'the emergence of a traumatic moment' (Freud 1964, p. 126), when, for whatever reason, the normal signalling fails. This is neurotic anxiety.

Taking into account Freud's three theories, it is generally agreed that he attributed the cause of anxiety to the powerlessness a child felt in the face of fear of loss of parental love. Freud's theories, therefore, can be illustrated as follows:

FEAR OF LOSS OF PARENTAL LOVE $\rightarrow$ POWERLESSNESS $\rightarrow$ REPRESSED ANXIETY.

## Otto Rank (Austria, 1884–1939)

Known for his impressive work on birth trauma, Rank believes that anxiety stems from the problem of individuation, or separation. For all people there is conflict between the desire to belong and the desire to be separate, the desire to be dependent and the desire to be independent; and while the majority of people handle their separation anxiety sufficiently to affirm themselves as autonomous individuals with exciting possibilities for growth in their own right, others never resolve the conflict and develop extreme or neurotic anxiety.

Commenting on Rank's theory about those who develop neurotic anxiety, Rollo May says there is 'anxiety in the face of individual autonomy ... and ... anxiety in the face of dependence on others' (1950, p. 152). An anxiety-sufferer has a 'great need to *appear independent* but at the same time to keep an actual excessive *dependence*' (1950, p. 152), and it is the constant conflict between these two that causes a child to feel powerless and confused. Her obsession with keeping everything in balance so as not to upset her parents, the guilt she feels whenever she exercises independence and autonomy, as well as the guilt she feels when she does *not* exercise independence and autonomy, are all experiences that render her powerless.

Rank's theory about the origin of severe anxiety, then, is that it is caused by feelings of powerlessness that result from the conflict a child experiences between wanting to be independent and wanting to remain dependent.

CONFLICT BETWEEN WANTING TO BE INDEPENDENT AND WANT-ING TO REMAIN DEPENDENT → POWERLESSNESS → REPRESSED ANXIETY

### Alfred Adler (Austria, 1870–1937)

According to Adler, neurotic anxiety develops as a result of one's evaluation of oneself as inferior. The inferiority he speaks of is not inferiority as fact, but rather, a *belief* that one is inferior. 'It does not matter . . . whether an individual is really inferior or not. What is important is his *interpretation* of his situation' (Adler 1928, p. 150). So, instead of developing an awareness of the self as having inferiority feelings ('I *feel* inferior'), the neurotic anxiety-sufferer develops an awareness of the self as inferior ('I *am* inferior').

Adler goes on to say that this kind of negative self-evaluation develops out of the parents' attitudes to the child. Then, in what appears to be a rather harsh evaluation of children who show symptoms of anxiety, fear, timidity and so on, he says that such children are really only interested in ruling their parents, so that they can feel superior rather than inferior to them. He gives an example of a child who screams during the night because of fear of the darkness. 'The child demands that someone should turn on the lights', he says. 'So long as one obeys, his anxiety is dispelled, but the moment his sense of superiority is threatened, he becomes anxious again, and through his anxiety fortifies his commanding position' (1928, p. 237).

Rollo May comments on Adler's contention that anxiety is often used by children (and adults) for the purpose of getting their own way, as an oversimplification of the problem. He suggests Adler must never have 'experienced or witnessed genuine

attacks of anxiety . . . [if he believes] that such panics are pro-
duced chiefly for the benefit of their effects upon others' (May
1950, p. 156).

Adler's evaluation of parents who respond with concern to
their child's anxiety is equally harsh. The fact that a child is
motivated to behave in such a way, he says, 'is a sign that one has
not allowed the child to develop any independence of spirit'
(Adler 1928, p. 236). This kind of thinking leads Adler to the
conclusion that anxiety neurosis in adult life is always due to a
person's having been a 'pampered' child. Again, Rollo May calls
this 'another example of his tendency toward oversimplification'
(May 1950, p. 157).

Adler's oversimplification of the problem does give the
impression that he may, in fact, have been referring to situations
of normal anxiety or fear, rather than severe anxiety. Given that
possibility, one might well ask: Why is his theory included here
at all? The reason is that while his suggestion that severe anxiety
is always caused by the 'pampered child' syndrome fails to hold
up under scrutiny, it has, nevertheless, prompted me to explore
more carefully the kinds of relationships anxiety-sufferers had, as
children, with their parents. What I can say, from my own
research with anxiety-sufferers, is that it is almost always true
that there has been an *unusual* relationship between parents and
child. The following examples will be helpful.

First, the unusual relationship often is, as Adler suggests, that
the child has been a pampered child. Several of the people I have
worked with have spoken of having been *the favourite child* in the
family, of having absolutely no complaints about their childhood, except occasionally feeling guilty about getting more
attention than their siblings. What they remember about their
childhood is that it was full of love and attention and indulgence.
They have difficulty remembering anything negative. When I
suggest, in the therapy setting, that all that attention must have
set up some sort of conflict for them, they shy away from any
such thoughts. They seem to have extreme difficulty allowing
themselves to be critical of their parents in any way at all, and
consequently do not want to hear that their parents may have
caused them conflict. Just the thought of criticising their parents

in that way makes them feel incredibly guilty—and anxious. The need in 'pampered' people to be their parents' protectors is very strong indeed.

The perception of oneself as the favoured child, the one in whom the parents have invested so much of their own energy, their own hopes and dreams, their own sense of fulfilment, does set up for a child a conflict between not wanting to let parents down and, at the same time, feeling unable ever to measure up to their expectations. Such a conflict can cause overwhelming feelings of powerlessness.

Another example of an unusual relationship with parents is one that is the opposite of the first example, and that is the situation of the unfavoured child, *the emotionally neglected child*, the one whose emotional needs were never given adequate attention. This kind of emotional neglect often occurs in a child who is required to be the strong one in the family, the one who can always be depended upon to be responsible, to take care of the other children, to take care of the parents when necessary, to take over the management of the home when parents are not able to cope.

The requirement to be parent to one's own siblings is difficult enough, but to have to be parent to one's own parents is a very heavy burden indeed for any child to bear. Again, the conflict is the same as for the 'pampered' child, and that is, the conflict between not wanting to let one's parents down, but feeling unable to measure up to the demands the situation places upon the child.

Another example of an unusual relationship between parent and child, and one which is always extremely destructive for the child, is that which occurs when she is *a victim of child sexual abuse.* When sexual demands are made on her by her father, step-father, grandfather, uncle, older brother or any other adult, her relationship with both parents becomes confused. When the perpetrator is her father or substitute father, a girl is forced into a kind of relating that she does not understand.

Once carefree and happy and trusting as only children can be, now she is always on guard, always fearful, always dreading the next time it might happen. Because of the father's crime against her, because he has thought it his right to force himself on her physically, sexually and sometimes emotionally, the father/daughter relationship has become one where his power and her total powerlessness are amplified. The girl knows that what is happening is wrong because of the extreme secrecy that surrounds it, but is powerless to stop it. In most instances, she feels afraid, confused, lonely and guilty. Often she plans to run away, but is afraid. She wants to tell somebody so that it will stop, but feels totally and utterly powerless.

In a study conducted in the state of Victoria in 1985, one fact that became obvious was 'how simple it was for the offenders to create a sense of guilt in their victim's minds which enabled the offenders to continue their sexual harassment with impunity' (Heath 1985, p. 57). The following are examples of the things victims were told after they had been molested:

- If you tell your mother it will kill her.
- Don't tell your mother or it will cause problems between the whole family.
- Don't tell the police or the family will break up and it will be your fault.
- If you tell anyone I will have to leave the family.

(Heath 1985, p. 57)

It was also found that violence or threats of violence are used extensively by perpetrators of child sexual abuse. In this same study, 'A young girl gave in to her father because he threatened to beat up her mother unless the girl did what he wanted. One girl believed that if she told anyone, her parents' marriage would break up and her mother would have a nervous breakdown' (Heath 1985, p. 58). The kinds of threats made by perpetrators include:

- If you tell anyone I will kill you.
- Don't tell anyone or you will cop it.
- Don't tell your mother or I will break your neck.
- If you tell anyone you will be in trouble and I will put you in a home.

- If anyone finds out I will go to prison and so will you.

(Heath 1985, p. 58)

Emotional blackmail is also used extensively. In the same study, it was found that 'emotional blackmail took the form of one offender threatening to kill himself if the girl didn't have sex with him. Another managed to coerce his daughter into having sex with him by saying she was the only thing that kept him going and that he would commit suicide if she didn't let him do it' (Heath 1985, p. 58).

A child who is the victim of her father's sexual abuse is forced into a way of relating with her father that is confusing and extremely stressful. In addition to that, her father's actions have also forced her into an unusual kind of relating with her mother. Whereas once her talk with her mother was open, spontaneous and trusting, now she has a secret she must keep from her at all costs. Forced to be guarded in what she says for fear of the consequences, she feels guilty in relation to her mother because she is involved in something she knows would make her mother very unhappy. It is also a fact that even though she is afraid to tell her mother, at some level she hates her mother for not knowing about it and making it stop.

The girl's relationship with both mother and father is thrown into chaos because of the actions of her father. She feels totally powerless, and because she believes her father's threats, her powerlessness is made worse by the knowledge that if she did anything to ease her own situation, she could destroy her family, make her mother very unhappy, and send her father to jail. Such a dilemma is too great for any child to bear.

One final example of an unusual parent/child relationship that some anxiety-sufferers have experienced in childhood is one where the *intimacy demands* of one or both of the parents on the child were overwhelming. Just as the demand for sexual intimacy constitutes sexual abuse of a child, the demand for emotional intimacy beyond which a child is capable constitutes emotional abuse. This kind of emotional abuse occurs when a child is constantly sought out by one of the parents to fulfil the role of confidante, or best friend, or 'the only person I can tell my inner secrets to—the only person who understands me'.

It is not unusual for this to happen in situations where a parent feels lonely, misunderstood, isolated from other adults, or where a parent is going through the break-up of a relationship, or is socially inept, and so on. It also occurs with some parents who are alcoholics or heavy drinkers. Those whose habit it is to be overcome with melancholy every time they drink to excess often insist that their children sit and listen to their drunken ramblings for as long as they choose to indulge themselves. Often a child is deeply disturbed by the parent's distress, but feels helpless to do anything to comfort the adult. Similarly, a child of a mentally ill person witnessing her parent's confusion and deep despair often feels pressure to make things better, and consequently experiences feelings of hopelessness and helplessness.

All of these demands for emotional intimacy or personal comfort are too much for a child, and in every instance, a conflict exists between not wanting to let the parent down but feeling unable to measure up, unable to help, unable to handle such a great responsibility.

CONFLICT BETWEEN NOT WANTING TO LET PARENTS DOWN, BUT FEELING UNABLE TO MEASURE UP → POWERLESSNESS → REPRESSED ANXIETY

### Karen Horney (Germany, 1885–1952; lived in the United States from 1932)

Horney refers to anxiety neurosis as 'basic anxiety', basic in the sense that 'it develops in early life out of disturbed relationships between the child and significant individuals in his personal environment, normally his parents. The typical conflict leading to anxiety in a child is that between dependency on the parents . . . and hostile impulses against the parents' (May 1950, p. 162). Hostility against parents has to be repressed because of the child's dependence, and 'such repression contributes to the child's feeling of defenselessness and helplessness' (1950, p. 163). In Horney's terms, basic anxiety is 'inseparably interwoven with a basic hostility' (Horney 1937, p. 89).

A very important contribution made by Horney to the understanding of neurotic anxiety is her suggestion that children develop 'neurotic trends' (Horney 1939, p. 199), or 'defensive tendencies' (Horney 1937, p. 101), in an attempt to repress their hostile feelings toward their parents. A child 'covers up his grudge against his own family . . . by conforming with his parents' attitudes' (1937, p. 89). In this instance, the 'defence' or 'cover-up' takes place when the child conforms.

Horney states that 'in our culture . . . [there are] four ways of protecting one's self against anxiety', and they are as follows:

> There are those whose foremost striving is to be loved or approved of, and who go to any length to have this wish gratified; those whose behavior is characterized by a tendency to comply, to give in and take no steps of self-assertion; those whose striving is dominated by the wish for success or power or possession; and those whose tendency is to shut themselves off from people and to be independent of them (1937, p. 102).

There is nothing wrong, she says, with wanting to be loved, wanting to comply, striving for success or needing to withdraw. The problem exists when these normal human drives acquire a 'protective function' (1937, p. 103).

Rollo May speaks of such protective functions or defensive tendencies in terms of the development of 'neurotic defenses' (May 1950, p. 163). A child develops a defensive pattern of behaviour such as smiling a lot, being 'good' all the time, obsessively complying with parents' wishes and so on as an attempt at ordering the world in such a way as to feel less powerless, and therefore more secure. The child's security rests upon the maintenance of that neurotic pattern. So long as nothing happens to threaten that pattern the child, and then the adult, can continue to defend against the return of those early, unbearable feelings of defenselessness, helplessness and powerlessness. It is when something does happen to shatter that security pattern (usually in adulthood) that the first anxiety attack occurs. In Horney's words, 'anything may provoke anxiety which is likely to jeopardize the individual's specific protective pursuits, his specific neurotic trends' (1939, pp. 198–9).

For example, if being totally devoted to parents and family worked for you as a child, if that helped you defend against anxiety, you will take that pattern with you into your marriage and be totally devoted to your spouse and children. This will work well for you, until you are confronted with the threat of losing your partner or children. The threat of losing one's partner can take many forms: the realisation that he is spending more and more time at work and showing less and less interest in you and the children; evidence that he may be having an affair; illness; sudden death of a male friend of a similar age; and so on. The threat of losing your children can occur: when you have a difficult pregnancy; when the youngest child starts school; when the oldest leaves home; when the youngest leaves home; when a child talks of suicide; when a friend's child dies suddenly; and so on.

While anxiety attacks are often associated with loss, it is important to point out that it is not the loss or threat of loss as such that causes the anxiety, but *the shattering of the neurotic pattern* on which a person's security has depended since very early in childhood. This explains why one person can experience loss after loss in life and never develop severe anxiety, while another is devastated by anxiety after only one experience of loss.

An example given by Rollo May is as follows: If, as a child, your basic anxiety could be allayed only by the unqualified admiration and reassurance of your parents, 'anxiety will arise at the prospect of being thrust into a situation in which [you are] unrecognized and unadmired' (May 1950, p. 164). When one finds oneself in a situation where the neurotic security pattern developed in childhood to defend against anxiety no longer works, the result is usually an anxiety attack followed by a prolonged period in which severe anxiety dominates one's life.

CONFLICT BETWEEN DEPENDENCE ON PARENTS AND HOSTILE IMPULSES AGAINST THE PARENTS $\rightarrow$ POWERLESSNESS $\rightarrow$ REPRESSED ANXIETY

The following formula has been developed from the above psychoanalytic theories, based in particular on the theory of Karen Horney:

95

feelings of powerlessness in childhood
(caused by fear of loss of parental love; conflict
between wanting to be independent and wanting to
remain dependent; conflict between not wanting to let
parents down but feeling unable to measure up;
and/or conflict between dependence on parents and
hostile impulses against the parents.)

+

development of a neurotic pattern (a security pattern)

+

a traumatic (un-planned for) event

↓

destruction of security pattern

↓

return of feelings of powerlessness

↓

anxiety attack (severe anxiety condition)

## Women's experiences of powerlessness

In adulthood, daily experiences of powerlessness are common in the lives of *all* women (not just anxiety-sufferers). They are so common that anyone who did develop a defensive pattern in childhood to protect herself from feelings of powerlessness has a very strong chance of being involved in situations in adulthood that have the potential for shattering that defence pattern and causing severe anxiety. The following real-life stories are included for the purpose of illustrating the prevalence of experiences that reinforce women's powerlessness on a day-to-day basis. It is important to emphasise here that the women who wrote these stories are not, to my knowledge, anxiety-sufferers. They are ordinary women writing about the ordinary (painful) experiences of their lives.

For the purposes of this study, a group of women of different ages, representing a variety of different lifestyles, were invited to

96

think about occasions in their lives when they experienced powerlessness, invisibility and emotional deprivation, and then to
write three of those incidents down as they remembered them—
one recounting an experience of powerlessness, another of invisibility, and the third of emotional deprivation. Some of the group
chose to write about one incident only, but most submitted a
story on each of the three topics.

While those stories written about invisibility and emotional
deprivation will appear in subsequent chapters, those describing
women's everyday experiences of powerlessness are included
here.

The first two stories are about *powerlessness in childhood*, utterly
desperate, paralysing powerlessness, the memory of which
remains fresh in these women's minds to this day:

> Powerlessness. Having to stand, sit or lie still (aged six) while
> a seventy-year-old man (that horrible sour old man's smell)
> dug his hard, yellowed and horned thumb into my tiny vagina.
> Tearing pain, fear, paralysis, betrayal—all, quite literally,
> unspeakable. Not knowing what else to do but be still, frozen.
> And for years hating myself for not being able to stop it.
> Hating *myself* for being powerless.

The second story recalls the experience of a fifteen-year-old
schoolgirl whose progress through most of her school life had
been hampered by her very poor eyesight.

> My idea was a simple, logical solution to my problem. All I
> wanted was for him to use the blackboard on the girls' side
> of the classroom to show the working for maths problems.
>
> I wouldn't be able to see clearly even then, but I had more
> chance of making sense of what was going on and could use
> my good memory and intelligence to cope in class, and later
> work through everything more fully at home . . .
>
> I was very scared of this man though. He sarcastically
> berated anyone who didn't follow his explanations and I'd
> already been one of his victims. How I churned inside with
> hurt, rage and despair at his attitude, for, not only did he
> discount my disability, he also taunted me with it . . .
>
> He barely gave me his attention while I outlined my plan,
> but his refusal was instant and dismissive. I made to protest

but was shocked and quickly silenced by the anger he turned on me. Forty years later, I can still feel his power reaching out to crush my spirit.

Several of the stories told of incidents of *powerlessness within personal relationships* with partners and also with other family members:

In the mid 1980s, I seemed to hit a point of powerlessness that reduced me to a walking, working frame of a person.

I felt I had shrunk down to the movements my body made and nothing more. I continued to work, to run the home and care for the kids, but the soul of ME was squeezed in to a small space somewhere inside my body. I felt so little and non-existent. I moved out of the house and into my car. I retreated to the car whenever I wasn't doing any of my duties.

Although the kids needed lots of reassurance, my husband just ignored the whole situation, ate the meals I prepared and moved about the house and yard as if I didn't exist.

After a week I got anxious about my behaviour and went to a marriage counsellor. He was amazed at my story and kept shaking his head. He had no idea what I was talking about or feeling. I came away feeling bizarre and alone.

Looking back, it is as if the 'I' of me wasn't there. Just the figure that performed the roles of housewife, mother, worker was present. Fortunately, I found the ME again, and never want to be that powerless again.

We were on a day's outing—my car—but he was driving. We stopped to get petrol and I asked him to check the pressure in the tyres, but it was raining and he wouldn't, even though I asked several times. (Subsequently, I learnt to check my own tyres, but at that time, I still subscribed to the myth that this was a complex and technical task!)

As we drove along narrow, winding mountainous roads, the mist and rain really set in and, even though we had two young children in the car, he refused to slow down. He continued driving at speeds I considered quite dangerous but which he claimed were safe. He knew what he was doing.

Another couple, friends of ours, sat quietly and anxiously in the back seat, and the tension in the car mounted. Their presence, and that of the children, served to quieten my protests to an acceptably polite tone, but inside I was furious that my wishes and my concerns were being so thoroughly ignored—and it was my vehicle!

In this situation, I felt totally without power or influence, and without any means of venting my outrage! I will never forget it.

From my earliest teenage memories until the age of 20 when I married, my one and only goal in life was to find true love, marry and have a family. I would then be secure, have attained success and be able to take my rightful place in the world. I would have the power over my life I so desperately longed for.

When I was twenty, I met a young man who was different to any man I had ever known. He was sensitive, caring and emotionally open. We were compatible in all the ways that mattered. Before long we conceived our first child and decided to get married.

At that time we were living on the other side of Australia from our families, and although we were very naive about the realities of life, we did cope in our own way. Many times I have wished we had maintained this distance, but we didn't. We decided to go home and become part of the extended family.

From the moment my feet left the last step of the plane, my life belonged to everyone but me. The church was chosen, the reception planned, the rings bought, the honeymoon decided, the flat where we would live after the honeymoon rented, with little or no consultation with me. During this frenzy of activity, I was suffering from morning sickness and a steadily growing depression. I felt totally and utterly powerless. The outcome of my life depended entirely on decisions made by those around me. I became unable to assert myself. It is little wonder that my long awaited wedding day was one of the most unhappy days of my life.

I remained in this dependent, powerless state for thirteen years. At that time I became involved as a volunteer in an organisation which helps people in crisis. My motivation for joining was to help others, but first I was required to learn about myself. Since then my feelings about myself have changed dramatically. I now take my place in life as a strong, independent woman.

Recently, I discussed this period of my life with my husband. He was very surprised to hear how I had been affected, because the exact opposite had happened to him. He sees that time as the beginning of his adult life, where he was expected to make important decisions, accept responsibility and take control of his (and my) life.

The last time I felt extreme powerlessness was when a boyfriend who I'd been involved with for about a year decided to end our relationship. We'd just been holidaying in New Zealand and I thought we were getting along quite well. I knew some of the excitement had disappeared, but overall I was happy with our relationship.

We were at his place, both helping to prepare dinner. He seemed very short tempered. I remember him having a go at me a couple of times about the way I was doing things.

Later, when we were eating, I asked if anything was wrong and at first he didn't want to talk about it. I pushed him a little and eventually he said that he didn't think things were working out with us and that he wanted to finish things.

I felt totally devastated. It just seemed to come totally 'out of the blue'. After some discussion about us breaking up, he actually asked me if I wanted to stay the night. To me, that seemed crazy. I drove home in tears and spent most of the night crying (and much of the next few days). What had I done wrong? Was there someone else? How could his feelings change so suddenly? How could he do this to me?

I've never really understood why it happened, but it was totally out of my control.

Then, there were stories about *powerlessness in the workplace:*

I had been working as a clerical assistant at the hospital for several months. It was a mundane, repetitive job but for the time being, it was paying the bills. It seemed to me that a great deal of intelligence was not needed, nor expected of women carrying out this work. Within the very rigid confines of the hospital hierarchy, based on patriarchal ideas of status, clerical assistants were close to the bottom.

One day as I was sorting through pieces of paper for the doctors to sort through to give back to us to sort through again, I decided that there may be an easier and more efficient way of doing this. I mentioned my idea to the sister-in-charge. I was not prepared for the blustering, the red face, the accusations of 'upstart' and 'who do you think you are?' 'The doctors must do that.' I stood, disbelieving, and actually shaking from the fury of her blast.

To add insult to injury I was then ordered around to the supervisor's office to be chastised again, loudly and therefore publicly. I felt like a small school child sent to the principal's office. I didn't feel stupid for I knew I had made a valid suggestion. I felt so frustrated and powerless that so little was expected of me and my position, and that so much status was placed on 'the doctors' that there was no room for flexibility. I learnt that nothing was to be questioned.

I was a government solicitor in an office that dealt with prosecutions. I was working towards becoming a barrister. I had spent two months preparing a complex matter for trial. I had taken the matter over from another prosecutor on top of my usual workload and had conducted the committal hearing, the preliminary hearing in the Magistrates Court. I told my supervisor that I really wanted to prosecute the trial myself, and that I was going to make sure I got admitted as a barrister prior to the trial so I could do so.

I worked like a Trojan, finishing off the requirements for my admission, filing applications and testimonials, posting notices in press, gazette and court, doing my usual workload, and preparing for the trial of a matter involving serious charges, 52 witnesses all over the country, complex questions of law, and new expert evidence which had not previously been accepted by a court. I was to be admitted the day before the trial was to start. I was excited but a little nervous at facing my first jury trial with a complex matter.

A week before the trial was to start, my supervisor told me that he intended to prosecute 'my' trial himself. He was to get the glory, I was to get some more unacknowledged slog. I was angry. He knew how much I wanted to do the trial, and he had left it till the last minute to tell me. I had no option but to comply, so I did what I had to, but treated him throughout that week with curtness and circumspection. He was used to positive stroking and ego-boosting from me.

He called me into his office two days before the trial started and berated me for my 'unprofessional and irrational behaviour'. He said, 'I don't know what's wrong with you. I can only presume that you are having some troubles at home, but this behaviour has got to stop. If it doesn't, I'll get someone else to help with this trial. I thought you would be happy to be part of the team with this one.'

I felt very unfairly treated. I could feel the tears welling up in my eyes. I didn't want to cry in front of him, and I knew I was on the verge of tears. I told him he could be sure I would do all that was required of me. I excused myself, left his room, went back into my room, shut the door and started to howl. Like a greyhound with the scent of dead rabbit in his nostrils he was opening my door in a flash—without knocking. He had one final verbal barb for me, and sneered silently at the unprofessional and emotional woman sobbing at her desk before him.

One was a story about a woman's *powerlessness in business dealings:*

A loan of $3000 was needed quickly if my husband and I were to take advantage of a car deal. My husband had been called out of town and, given the urgency of the situation, I made application in my name only. The bank officer had indicated that the loan would likely be approved that very afternoon.

At 5 pm the officer called to say that the money was certainly available, however, the loans manager had instead decided to credit our joint cheque account until my husband returned, at which time both of us were expected to sign a joint application form.

For a moment I was too surprised to be angry. I was employed, had an excellent credit rating and considerable joint assets. It had seemed to me, and to the officer, that an approval would be a mere formality. Feeling puzzled and finally resentful, I asked why my application had been rejected. The 'reason' was that I had listed joint assets rather than only my half-share of those assets—to my mind, a feeble technicality, and I said so.

In my heart I knew that, had my husband filed the application listing joint assets, the loan would have been granted.

Finally, one woman wrote about her feelings of *powerlessness in relation to control of her own body*:

I remember the day well. It started like any other day, until under the shower I discovered a lump in my breast. Immediately I went into an internal panic. There is a family history of breast cancer, my mother and three of her sisters had all died of it.

I avoided the problem for a few days and then made an appointment to see a doctor. My own doctor (female) was away, so I was passed on to another doctor in the practice (male). The appointment was for 9.30 am. After examination and checking on my family history, an immediate appointment was made with a specialist for 12 o'clock that day. I was not told anything, just a pat on the arm and a comment 'You'll be alright'. No explanation of why it was so urgent.

Dutifully at 12 midday I was at the specialist's rooms. After waiting about 45 minutes, I was ushered into the surgery. My history taken again, my breasts examined, a couple of mumbled words and the comment, 'Those lumps will have to come out, my girl—probably later today'.

By now, I was totally submissive in this situation, despite the fact that I was a highly intelligent woman who had worked in the medical world for a long time, knew my way around doctors and knew the right questions to ask.

At 4 pm that same day I was being wheeled into the operating theatre for an operation even though I had not been informed of the possible outcomes. I didn't know if they would do a frozen section (examination of the lump immediately for a rapid diagnosis of possible malignancy), remove the breast, or what. At no stage in that process was I consulted or informed about what was being done, or what was to be done, to my body.

On waking from the anaesthetic and finding, to my great relief, that I had not had my breast removed, I remember the incredible rage I felt at the way I had been treated. I had been placed in a situation of total powerlessness. I was just an object to be dealt with, not a human being or a woman.

Women reading these stories will probably identify in some way with all of them because of the fact that they represent a common theme in all women's lives. The reason for including such stories is to show anxiety-sufferers how easy it is for one's defence pattern, so carefully (yet unconsciously) constructed in childhood to protect oneself against feelings of anxiety, to be shattered. Any one of these ordinary, everyday experiences of women's powerlessness can be the one that finally triggers the development of the condition of severe anxiety in those who are predisposed to it.

After you, the anxiety-sufferer, have achieved a cure through following the treatment process in chapter 6, you may then feel ready to allow yourself to look at your own life-stories of powerlessness. Once you do that, and are prepared to acknowledge the damaging effects of continuing feelings of powerlessness in your life, the next step is that you will begin the search for ways of empowering yourself. To ensure that you are never as vulnerable again to the onset of severe anxiety, it is important that you give priority to improving your self-esteem, developing your self-confidence, learning how to be angry about your oppression, and discovering new and assertive ways of responding in every area of your life.

# 4

# Women's invisibility as cause

Invisibility is the word often used to describe the experience of not being: not being noticed, not being recognised, not being acknowledged, not being listened to, not being taken seriously. Any experience that causes a person to feel she is not worth anything—being ignored, talked over, interrupted, brushed aside, misrepresented, ridiculed, trivialised, and so on—is an experience of invisibility.

Women in our society are familiar with the feeling of invisibility for two reasons. One (as outlined in chapter 2) is that patriarchal society renders women invisible by giving attention almost exclusively to men and male meanings. The other is that women render themselves invisible by being all too ready to blend into the background and allow male meanings to predominate. The recorded history of the human race is an obvious example of the way society causes women to be invisible. The history we are taught as children is a detailed account of what men have done, while the stories of women through the ages have rarely been told. Women's knowledge has been suppressed and our meanings ignored. Women's naming of the world, even when that naming is of our own experiences, has been denied us and replaced by male definitions of our experiences. In Dale Spender's words, women's naming has been ' "disallowed" with the result that women—and their experience—have frequently been made invisible' (Spender 1980, p. 54).

*Motherhood* is an example used by Spender as indicative of the way official definitions overshadow the reality of women's experiences:

> The society in which many of us have been reared has a legitimated meaning for *motherhood* which means feminine fulfilment, which represents something beautiful, that leaves women consumed and replete with joy.
>
> . . . For many women motherhood may have been an entirely different experience. Such women may have generated alternative—even conflicting—meanings (and names) in relation to motherhood but their meanings have been without authority or validity. Such meanings then, may not have been handed down, or if they were, would not have carried the same weight as the legitimated ones.
>
> For those women for whom motherhood may have represented neither joy nor beauty, a substantial problem arises. There is no reference point for their experience, no way of making it seem real, with the result that they can be left feeling extremely inadequate, convinced that there is something wrong with themselves, because their meanings do not mesh with the accepted ones . . . (Spender 1980, p. 54).

*Childbirth* is another instance of the way in which official meanings can overshadow the reality of women's experience. For many women, the experience of childbirth represents excruciating pain and agony, incredible loneliness and alienation, but their meanings are rarely told because such meanings contradict the accepted definition of childbirth as beautiful, fulfilling and joyful. Women's real experience is made invisible.

The church's role in covering up and denying women's experience of childbirth, is made evident with the telling of the story of the birth of Christ. Every year, the Christmas story is used as an opportunity to glorify motherhood and paint a picture of childbirth as a wonderful, almost ethereal experience. After a problem-free delivery in a fairy-tale setting, we are led to believe that Mary is thrilled by the singing of the angels and overjoyed at the visits by shepherds and wise men. Told from the perspective of Mary herself, however, the story would probably be very different. She would talk about the pain, the discomfort, the smell of the stable, the lack of privacy, her concern about hygiene. She would express her annoyance at all those strangers visiting her when all she wanted was simply to be with her husband and baby. She would express her concern about all that loud angelic singing when what she really wanted, in her exhausted state, was to be left to sleep in peace while she could.

*Marriage* is yet another example where women's experience is denied, and replaced by a false but more socially acceptable meaning. The many myths that exist in society about women's experience of marriage include: marriage is a wonderfully fulfilling experience for women; marriage means having someone to share your life with, someone to care for you, someone to protect you, someone to love you and be there for you; marriage represents a stable, happy atmosphere in which to bring up your children; and so on. Such propaganda about the meaning of marriage is still effective even in the face of overwhelming evidence to suggest the propaganda is, in most instances, false.

One does not have to search very hard to find evidence that, for many women, the true meaning of marriage is more accurately described in terms of loneliness, disillusionment, frustration, low self-esteem, lack of emotional support—and for others, in terms of physical assault, hurt, pain, humiliation, sexual abuse, fear of death, even death itself.

Nevertheless, the myth of eternal happiness available to women through marriage is very strong and most women, even after one or more disastrous marriages, prefer to believe the myth rather than their own experience. The sad truth is that it is only possible for such a woman to continue believing the myth if she can convince herself that she and she alone was responsible for her bad experiences of the past, and that if she tries harder next time, the myth of the happy marriage will become a reality for her. While we continue to deny the truth of our own experiences, we are colluding with the patriarchy in making our meanings invisible. The effect of that is that no-one feels the need to give any attention to women and women's concerns, because they are virtually not there. They do not exist. They have been made invisible.

The reasons why women continue to render themselves

invisible are quite clear when one reminds oneself that we are taught such blending-into-the-background behaviour from early childhood. As children, we were left in no doubt that centre stage is for boys, and that our place is somewhere off-centre, not so close that we steal the limelight, but also not so far away that we cannot relate to the centre. A very important part of the off-centre role is that of relating to the centre so that the centre's visibility is maintained and enhanced.

By the time we reach adulthood, most of us have learned the art of chameleon-like behaviour so well that we do it automatically, and while we secretly object to being ignored, we seem by our silence actually to collude in our own invisibility. One of the most difficult things for a woman to do in attempting to raise her self-esteem and learning to be assertive is to stop accepting and colluding in her own invisibility, and to begin speaking out and insisting on her own visibility.

## Existential theory

Existential psychotherapeutic theory highlights the damaging psychological effects of what is referred to here as 'invisibility'. The experience of invisibility is, in existentialist terms, an experience of 'nonbeing', and the fear of nonbeing is said to be the main cause of severe anxiety. Every experience of invisibility is a reminder that one's identity as a person is tenuous, and that one's meaning and purpose in life can easily be brought to nothing.

The following discussion of existential theory about the cause of severe anxiety will focus on the work of Paul Tillich, American philosopher and theologian of the 1950s and early 1960s, and also of Rollo May, author and psychotherapist, whose work with clients in his New York practice was grounded in existential philosophy. It must be emphasised here that while existential theory often seems difficult to understand because of its particular terminology, anyone wanting to develop a greater understanding of the condition of severe anxiety must not ignore its very considerable contribution.

Anxiety is a major theme in existential philosophy, and therapists whose work is influenced by this school of thought speak of basic or existential anxiety on the one hand, and neurotic or pathological anxiety on the other.

## Normal (existential) anxiety

Focusing first on normal anxiety, existentialists believe that normal (existential) anxiety is basic to existence itself. A relevant premise would be: to exist is to be anxious, or, to put it another way, anxiety is a normal factor in being human.

### Fear of nonbeing

If anxiety is a normal factor in being human, an obvious question would be: Where does this anxiety originate? Paul Tillich explains that 'anxiety is the state in which a being is aware of its possible nonbeing', or in shorter form, 'anxiety is the existential awareness of nonbeing' (Tillich 1952, p. 35). In other words, everyone of us has an awareness deep down inside us that our existence is tenuous, that there is nothing certain about our existence, and that as beings we could at any time cease to be. When Tillich makes statements like, 'anxiety is the existential awareness of nonbeing', he is not referring to some abstract knowledge of nonbeing, but rather to this awareness in the depths of our selves that nonbeing is an integral part of our being, from which there is no escape. It is this awareness that we are at all times both being and nonbeing that causes us anxiety.

### Fear of becoming 'nothing'

Rollo May makes a comparison between Tillich's reference to anxiety as the 'fear of nonbeing', and Kierkegaard's statement that anxiety is the 'fear of nothingness', which May interprets to mean the 'fear of becoming nothing' (May 1950, p. 208). This comparison helps clarify what Tillich meant when he spoke of nonbeing, and makes it easier for us to relate his concept to our everyday lives. Most of us have some degree of awareness that there is the potential within us to 'become nothing', and would admit, if we thought about it, that it is the possibility of becoming nothing that we dread most in life.

May clarifies it even further when he goes on to point out that our nonbeing is illustrated to us in those events in our lives when we are forced to confront 'death, fatigue, illness, destructive aggression, etc.' (May 1950, p. 208). Such events remind us of our own vulnerability, and cause us anxiety.

> The normal anxiety associated in the minds of most people with death is, of course, the most universal form of this anxiety. But the dissolution of the self may consist not simply of physical death. It may consist also of the loss of psychological or spiritual meaning which is identified with one's existence as a self—i.e., the threat of meaninglessness (May 1950, p. 208).

*The role of loss*
Any kind of loss or potential loss, whether it be the potential loss of one's own life, the loss of a loved one through death, loss through separation or divorce, loss of health, loss of children who have grown up and left home, loss of a job, loss of reputation, loss of self-esteem, is a reminder to any person that she can never be totally in control of her own life, and that she cannot orchestrate things to make the world the way she wants it to be. It is a reminder that she is vulnerable and she is powerless. Any kind of loss or potential loss brings one face to face with the fact of one's own nonbeing, and causes anxiety.

*Three types of anxiety*
Tillich supports this notion in his chapter on 'Being, Nonbeing, and Anxiety', when he suggests there are three types of anxiety (Tillich 1952, pp. 40–54). The first is anxiety that comes when nonbeing threatens one's *ontic self-affirmation*, that is, threatens one's very existence as a being, through fate and death. 'The anxiety of fate and death is most basic, most universal, and inescapable. All attempts to argue it away are futile ... For existentially everybody is aware of the complete loss of self which biological extinction implies' (1952, p. 42). The knowledge that fate and death are inescapable is an ever-present reminder of nonbeing.

Thankfully, Tillich concludes his discussion of the first type of anxiety on a positive note when he leaves us with a clue as to how we might escape the anxiety of nonbeing. He asks: 'Is there a courage ... to affirm oneself in spite of the threat against [one's] ontic self-affirmation?' (1952, p. 45). *The courage to affirm oneself* is the clue to escaping the anxiety of nonbeing. This is a point we will see repeated over and over again as we proceed with our discussion of existential theory.

Second, there is anxiety that comes when nonbeing threatens one's *spiritual self-affirmation*, through emptiness and meaninglessness. Tillich paints a clear picture of emptiness as including restlessness, discontent, apathy, despair, when he says: 'Everything is tried and nothing satisfies' (1952, p. 48). Even worse than that, however, is the experience of meaninglessness. 'The anxiety of meaninglessness is anxiety about the loss of an ultimate concern, of a meaning which gives meaning to all meanings. This anxiety is aroused by the loss of a spiritual center, of an answer ... to the question of the meaning of existence' (1952, p. 47). No matter how frantically a person searches for some meaningful activity with which to fill the emptiness and take away the feeling of meaninglessness, nothing will bring peace and satisfaction to the one who has lost the meaning of who she really is. When one loses sight of oneself, one experiences the anxiety of meaninglessness in all its devastating reality.

It is here, in Tillich's second category of anxiety, that invisibility fits most comfortably. The experience of invisibility is a threat to one's spiritual existence, first in terms of emptiness, and then in terms of meaninglessness. When a woman is treated as if she is invisible, she experiences emptiness, and the more she is made to feel invisible the more intense and unbearable are her feelings of emptiness; but worse than that, when a woman treats herself as invisible, when she allows other people's treatment of her to affect her affirmation of herself, she opens herself up to the dreadful anxiety of meaninglessness. Again, the way to escape emptiness and meaninglessness is to have the courage to affirm oneself in spite of the threat of nonbeing. The answer to the threat of invisibility lies in self-affirmation.

Third, there is anxiety that comes when nonbeing threatens one's *moral self-affirmation*, through guilt, self-rejection and condemnation. Here Tillich speaks of our moral responsibility to make something of ourselves, to fulfil our destiny. He says, 'in

111

every act of moral self-affirmation' we contribute to the fulfilment of our destiny, to the actualisation of what we potentially are (1952, p. 52), but at the same time we are aware that 'nonbeing is mixed with being' (1952, p. 52) and that we could just as easily act for evil as for good. This awareness produces the feeling of guilt. Worse than that, 'the anxiety of guilt . . . can drive us toward complete self-rejection, to the feeling of being condemned—not to an external punishment but to the despair of having lost our destiny' (Tillich 1952, pp. 52–3).

## The need for self-affirmation

Having discussed the anxiety of nonbeing as it relates to experiences of fate, death, emptiness, meaninglessness, guilt, self-rejection and condemnation, Tillich goes on to explain that what we need to do is incorporate our anxiety about nonbeing into ourselves. Instead of trying to avoid it or ignore it, we need to acknowledge it as a normal part of who we are. He talks about courageously taking the anxiety of nonbeing into one's self-affirmation (1952, p. 66). In other words, we are to affirm ourselves as beings who are made up of both being and nonbeing. Whatever we experience in life, even when it is an experience of nonbeing, we are to affirm ourselves in spite of it.

The good news is that the overwhelming majority of people, without even being aware of it, do exactly that—they get on with their lives in spite of the anxiety of nonbeing. They take the bad with the good, and continue to find strength and hope in self-affirmation. The anxiety these people experience is normal anxiety.

## Severe (neurotic) anxiety

On the other hand, there are people who have extreme difficulty accepting nonbeing as a normal part of life and incorporating it into themselves. They become highly sensitised to the experiences of nonbeing, and instead of developing an attitude which says: 'Whatever happens in my life is all right', they use up huge amounts of energy trying to avoid and ignore any hint of nonbeing. These are the people whose anxiety is neurotic and who develop the condition we refer to here as severe anxiety.

The fact is that when one sets about to avoid nonbeing, one is able to do so only by avoiding being. Tillich says, 'Neurosis is the way of avoiding nonbeing by avoiding being' (1952, p. 66). He makes the point that, by escaping into neurosis, 'the self which is affirmed is a reduced one' (1952, p. 66), a fact which is confirmed over and over again by anxiety-sufferers who admit that this condition drastically reduces their capacity for living life to the full. They build up, either in childhood or in adult life, what Tillich calls a 'fragmentary courage with which . . . (to master) objects of fear' (1952, p. 69). In other words they develop defences, or patterns of behaviour, which help them cope with situations that otherwise would cause anxiety.

It is important to note, at this point, the similarity between existential theory and the psychoanalytic theory of Karen Horney. Both Tillich and Horney agree that anxiety-sufferers develop coping mechanisms, and so long as nothing happens to shatter the way they have ordered their world, life can go along very well. However, as soon as change occurs over which they have no control, or as soon as there is the potential for change, the world they have constructed for themselves no longer feels safe.

The thing about life, of course, is that changes do happen all the time, and just as there is no way to shield oneself against change, there is also no way to defend oneself against nonbeing. Defences certainly do help a person cope, but as Tillich says, we are always affected 'by the reality which permanently penetrates the castle of (our) defense . . .' (1952, p. 69). The reality of nonbeing is always there penetrating our defences. We cannot escape from it.

In practical terms, the same kind of example used to illustrate Horney's theory would be relevant here: We begin with a woman who has never learnt to incorporate nonbeing into her life. She has a husband and children who are, in fact, her defence against the nonbeing of loneliness, invisibility, emptiness and meaninglessness. She copes very well, and life is reasonably good. One day it occurs to her that her children have grown up and will be leaving home in the next year or so, or it occurs to her that her husband is the same age as a couple of his friends who recently had heart attacks and died suddenly. This woman is a prime candidate for developing anxiety attacks.

The important point about this example, and the point on which Horney and Tillich agree, is that it is not simply the fear of losing her husband and children that would cause this woman to begin having anxiety attacks. (Many women face that fear and come through it unhindered by neurosis.) Rather, it is the fact that she would be losing that which gave her a sense of security against anxiety, that which held her fragile life together, that which helped her defend against nonbeing, that which enabled her to ignore the reality of nonbeing in her life.

Existentialism reminds us that we cannot get away from nonbeing, because it is as real as being itself. Unhappiness, loneliness, invisibility, emptiness, meaninglessness, sickness and death are just as real and have just as much right to be incorporated into one's self as happiness, love, visibility, fulfilment, meaningfulness, health and life.

## The need to strengthen one's sense of self

While existential theory does not attempt to present any practical, step-by-step treatment method, its emphasis on the need for anxiety-sufferers to strengthen their sense of self is of great importance. Repeating Tillich's emphasis on the need for self-affirmation, he says there must first be a willingness to acknowledge nonbeing, followed by 'a powerful self-affirmation in spite of the anxiety of nonbeing' (1952, p. 66). Similarly, May says, '... when this form of anxiety is confronted affirmatively— when the individual both realizes the *threat* of meaninglessness and takes *a stand against the threat*—the result is a strengthening of the individual's experience of selfhood' (May 1950, p. 16).

Of invisibility, the same thing can be said: When a woman realises the threat of invisibility and takes a stand against the threat, the result is a strengthening of her experience of self. As a woman works to improve her self-esteem and refuses to accept the anxiety brought on by experiences of invisibility, she confidently and assertively affirms herself and establishes her visibility in spite of the powers of nonbeing.

114

## Women's experience of invisibility

Every experience of invisibility brings one face to face with the threat of nonbeing and, therefore, the power such experiences have to degrade and destroy must never be underestimated. Because invisibility is such a common experience for women in male-oriented societies, women are constantly engaged in a struggle to affirm themselves, just to survive psychologically and emotionally. The following stories are everyday examples of women's invisibility, written by the same group of women who wrote about powerlessness in chapter 3. To reiterate, these women are not, to my knowledge, anxiety-sufferers. They are ordinary women living ordinary lives, who were asked simply to recall an incident in which they experienced the feeling of invisibility.

Some of the stories submitted were about *invisibility in childhood*, and as with all traumatic childhood experiences, the memory of these incidents still remains fresh in these women's minds:

My sister Fay, and I, at about ages seven and eight, were helping Mum pack the annual Christmas parcel that was to be sent to Dad's brother in England. I was reviewing the envelope of family photos that was to accompany the gifts.

Dad had inscribed on the back of each photo a short note indicating persons, place and event—'Fay and Robin skating on back pond', 'Pat (Mum) and I at Halloween party'. Flipping over the photo of Dad holding Jack, our nine-month old brother, I read, 'At last, a son and heir!' My heart flopped, instantly deflated at the words, 'At last'. Not only did I feel I was a kind of 'second prize', but I recognised the implicit impossibility of ever being able to achieve this obviously valuable thing of 'son and heir'.

Until that moment, my secret script had said to me that, as the eldest and also my father's namesake, I was prime in his affections and hopes. That inscription now became *knowledge* that I was not 'good enough', and worse, that I could never become good enough.

I was the only girl in a class of 23 studying Maths 2 in High School. I always sat at the back of the class because I felt that I didn't belong. The boys would tell jokes that were tamely sexual, but they would always have connotations about women that would make me feel uncomfortable.

The teacher was a man who took army reserve training for some of the war heads at the school. He had been in the army. Sometimes he wore his 'greens' into the classroom. He always conducted the class with a sort of clipped sternness. He would stride up and down the rows.

I felt like I wasn't really there. No one ever sat next to me, and no other student ever talked to me like an equal. They would sometimes leer at me, sometimes mock me, sometimes tease me.

I remember that I couldn't come to terms with complex numbers, and while everyone else was working on their problems, I sat at the back of the class, anxious and worried, and not being able to start.

The teacher strode over to my desk and said, 'Why aren't you working?' I told him I couldn't understand how to do the sums. He told me I must not have listened, I must have been dreaming when he was talking. He told me I would have to read the chapter again that night at home. I had been listening. I had read the chapter. I just couldn't understand.

I really believed at that time, that if you were a boy, you could do these hard things, you could understand this sort of puzzle. If you were a girl, you were just lost and silly, so far as complex numbers were concerned.

When I was about fourteen, my mother was a very active member of a fundamentalist christian religion. She was separated from my father, and was having a difficult time raising three teenage daughters alone. Mum liked to look after people, so she would often provide meals and company for men from the church, especially those without wives and mothers to care for them. One man who visited a lot was in his late forties. His wife had been excommunicated from the church because of her adultery. He was forbidden to have contact with her.

One day, I was sitting on my mother's bed as she was showing this man a window that needed repairing. He had offered to fix it. They were having a long conversation. Mum walked out of the room, talking as she went. I went to follow her. He was behind me. As I walked out of the door, he grabbed hold of me and pushed me behind the door. His big hairy hands groped at my small breasts. His thick square body pushed into my back. His right hand reached between my legs and he grabbed at my crotch. I was menstruating and wearing a sanitary pad. I knew his groping, grasping hands could feel the thick wad of the pad.

I felt embarrassed, invaded, repulsed and numb. My mother was outside in the kitchen talking away. He had answered her while his hands were gnawing at me. Suddenly, he pushed me aside and walked out into the kitchen. My mother was still talking. Their conversation hadn't missed a beat. His face was impassive, not one trace of any reaction to what he had done. I was numb. I was speechless. I just seemed to disappear for a while.

Some of the stories were about incidents of *invisibility in personal relationships*:

I can't believe that he does this to me. I know he's not ready to make a commitment, but ignoring our relationship when we're in public, well, it basically comes down to ignoring me. It was like there were two parts to our being together, and if I didn't put up with the one, I wouldn't get the other.

We were standing near the windows at the bar, when over walked an extremely attractive woman. He immediately preened. It was amazing. I could actually *see* the change. He stood taller, slightly separate from me, and pasted on his smile. That was it. I was no longer thought of. He didn't introduce me, he didn't look at me, he didn't touch me. I knew that if I had done something to make him acknowledge me, let alone make obvious the fact that we were lovers, I would lose him. I would be breaking his rules—rules he had made and to which I felt I had to conform.

I became locked into this position where our relationship was not acknowledged. No touching. No endearments. I was a 'friend'—which, in fact, made me a nobody.

117

In the 1960s, I remember going to a social evening with my husband's work colleagues in someone's home. The women sat in the lounge and discussed babies, shopping, housework, things that didn't interest me at that time. I wandered in to the kitchen where the men were talking about car engines. I joined the group and listened.

One of the men asked a question . . . I answered it . . . I knew the answer. My speaking made no ripple on the flow of the men's talk. The question was asked again, and this time answered by someone else. There was a kind of shuffle through the group, a kind of relief that the question had been answered. I remember standing there in the group asking myself, 'Am I here? Is this a dream? Perhaps I don't exist at all, and I just *think* I do'.

This feeling of not existing was reinforced in many ways. For some reason when I pushed a pram, I was invisible. I could see expressions of distaste on shopkeepers' faces as they registered the waving arms of the toddler and the child in the pram, all concern for the goods on low shelves—but *I* didn't impinge on their consciousness at all.

It was the same when I was pregnant. To doctors and nursing staff I was somehow negated as a person, becoming a protruding stomach. I feel really angry when I look back at the attitudes about women and childbirth then: a stiff upper lip, just get on with it, and don't you dare let any of your other duties slip just because you are pregnant. I feel cheated of the celebration and specialness of producing the next generation. Invisibility! I know about that feeling!

One of the women wrote about her experience of *invisibility in a group situation*:

As I sat in the small group listening to the speaker who had joined us for this session, I felt an all too familiar surge of anger rising like a wave to my head. Weren't we all supposed to be involved in this discussion? How come, then, that I can't catch the speaker's eye?

Thoughts rushed through my mind about the possible reasonable explanations like the fact that it's the angle of her chair, or she hasn't heard MY encouraging murmurings. So I leant forward. Sure enough, she glanced my way but then quickly looked away. At an appropriate moment, I made a relevant comment. She looked surprised and managed a nod of acknowledgment, but just as quickly she took my point up with another member of the group.

I felt a tightening in my chest, like my anger had shrunk inside me to be replaced with the pain of rejection. I felt as insignificant in that group as the leaf on the plant that stood wilting by the door.

I switched off to the issues being discussed. I heard the words but they had to compete in my consciousness with that other issue I constantly faced—the question of 'what's wrong with me?'

Several of the stories were about the women's experiences of *invisibility in work situations*:

Six years ago, I went to work in the office of a very small section of a university. There was only my boss and myself in the section at that time, and as the services offered to the students increased, we became very busy. My boss seemed to be very grateful that I was capable of doing work above and beyond that of my job classification, and depended on me more and more to assist him, and as time passed, to take over work which was previously his. Although there was never any monetary reward, I did get satisfaction from knowing I did my work well.

After three years it was recognised that assistance was needed to develop existing services, and a third person joined the staff. With the increasing numbers and needs of students each year, the service continued to grow, and we often talked about employing a fourth person. I had hopes that when this position was created, I would be considered as a suitable applicant and my efforts would be rewarded.

This position of administrative officer did eventuate, and has now been filled. It was never advertised. My boss gave it to a friend of his whom the university had found an embarrassment in the area he was employed in, and wanted to be rid of.

Last year, all the positions on campus were reevaluated in an attempt to update and reclassify as appropriate. We all had to fill out detailed forms outlining what our positions entailed according to given criteria. I was quite surprised to see all the duties I performed when they were actually written down on paper, and looked forward to some recognition. The outcome was that, as the service now employed an administrative officer, he would be responsible for the work I had done for six years, and *I would be his assistant.* My position was not upgraded, and I received no recognition for all my hard work.

Recently I applied for and obtained a position in another section of the university, which no doubt is a great relief to my ex-boss's conscience. I still feel very hurt.

My job entailed considerable contact with the supervisor of a large workgroup—most of it by phone. Part of my role was to supervise the supervisors, and over time, I had built up a constructive, supportive relationship with this man.

On a routine, pre-arranged visit to his work-site, I arrived with the boss. Despite our more regular contact, the supervisor walked directly up to the boss, extending his hand and greeting him warmly. I was ignored.

While I knew that this neglect of me was not generated by any negative feeling or lack of respect on the part of the supervisor, I was also aware that, in comparison with this large and powerful man who accompanied me, I was momentarily unimportant. I knew it was the way of the world with regard to women. Still I felt diminished.

In 1985, I was practising as a solicitor and I took a course which I needed to do to be admitted as a barrister. Part of the course involved presenting mock cases before magistrates who had volunteered to sit at night to play the role of magistrate, and to provide feedback to students. During one night a magistrate addressed me during a feedback session as 'Miss'. I told him that I did not use a title, but if one was absolutely necessary, I preferred to be addressed as 'Ms'.

The magistrate became agitated and told me, 'I don't care what sort of women's lib. nonsense you go on with outside my court, but in my court you may be "Miss" or "Mrs" and nothing else'. I was hurt and felt like a child who had no right even to determine how she wished to be addressed. I was angry that this man would not allow me that right and that courtesy. He had deprived me of my identity.

The devil in me wanted to say, 'Well sir, in view of my statutory status as a "gentleman" once I become a barrister, you may address me as "Mr".' However, I simply said nothing and gritted my teeth, wondering whether I would always compromise myself so in my practice of the law.

As a young graduate I joined a deadened old university department, as a tutor. I was filled with a love of the subject, with all my experiences as an undergraduate, with a strong desire to reform . . . it was a very sexist, unfriendly place.

I was naive in my expectations of change. I was unaware of the entrenched hierarchies. I thought the staff meetings would be run on democratic principles. I spoke. I didn't know that as an untenured tutor (lowest of all) I should never open my mouth. I thought they'd welcome a fresh perspective. They hated me. So they simply refused to hear me.

One staff member would speak. I would speak. Then another staff member would respond to the points made by the person who'd spoken before me. As if I had not uttered a word, or as if I'd yelled down a long tunnel and no-one could hear. Except that they could hear, they just chose not to. Sometimes, later in a meeting, a staff member would repeat a point I'd made earlier, always without acknowledgement. It would be greeted as a new idea, with no hint that it had been voiced before.

I persevered for three and a half years, with a paralysing headache after every meeting. Then I stopped attending. I've often wondered if they even noticed.

In 1988 I was working as a government veterinary officer in a small Queensland country town. My job mostly involved working with cattle. I thought I had quite a high public profile as the fact that I was blonde, attractive, single, young and a woman had attracted public comment when I had been appointed. I had also published articles in the local press and spoken on radio about veterinary related matters.

One morning a grazier called the office and spoke to my boss. He was anxious because a lot of his cattle were dying. I was sent to investigate. There were no departmental stockies available to help, so I went on my own in the four wheel drive, properly equipped to meet any contingency on my own with some help from the grazier.

As I pulled up at the homestead gate in the usual cloud of red dust, the cocky walked out to the gate to meet the car which carried the work logo on the front doors. I got out of the car, walked toward him, introducing myself. He stood silently frowning. I asked if anything was wrong. He looked through me with a puzzled look on his face. He squinted in the direction of the car, looked to the left and then to the right of me, and then said, 'There must be some mistake. They told me they were sending a vet.'

Anxiety-sufferers, reading these stories, will be reminded of how easily a person's defence pattern can be shattered. A simple incident of invisibility, where one is ignored, brushed aside, not recognised, not appreciated, not included, can be the 'last straw'. Usually the incident that triggers severe anxiety is one of a long line of incidents over a period of months or years. After many similar experiences of nonbeing, there comes a time when a woman who has been unable to incorporate nonbeing into her being, is no longer able to defend against her anxiety. It breaks through her defence and she suffers an anxiety attack. It is not the experience of invisibility as such that causes the anxiety attack, but the unbearable feelings of emptiness and meaningless-ness that usually accompany such experiences.

All women living in male-dominated western societies who want to avoid the emptiness and meaninglessness caused by experiences of invisibility, must find the courage to affirm themselves, to strengthen their experience of selfhood, in spite of the threat of nonbeing.

# 5

# Women's emotional deprivation as cause

Emotional deprivation is another common experience among women and begins early in life with the psychological demands placed on them in the process of social conditioning. Luise Eichenbaum and Suzie Orbach, feminist therapists working at the Women's Therapy Centre in London, identify three demands that flow from a woman's social role. One is that 'she must *defer* to others—follow their lead, articulate her needs only in relation to theirs' (Eichenbaum & Orbach 1983, p. 7). A result of this deferring to others is that it then becomes difficult for women to recognise their own needs, and 'a process often occurs in which *women come to hide their desires from themselves*' (1983, p. 8).

A second demand is that 'she must always be *connected* to others and shape her life in accordance with a man's. A woman's status will derive from that of her mate. Indeed, her very sense of self and well-being may rely on her connection with him' (1983, p. 8). In order that the connection to others is maintained, she 'must make herself into a person others will find pleasing; (but) in making herself in their image she may end up not knowing who she is. *She loses herself*' (1983, p. 9). It is important to note that both of the requirements mentioned so far result in invisibility and emotional deprivation: *deferring* to others results in women 'hiding their desires from themselves', while being *connected* to others results in women 'losing themselves'.

A third demand is that a woman have '*emotional antennae*. A woman must learn to anticipate others' needs' (1983, p. 9). Through her intuition, she must seek out and discover what they need, and then:

> Once she has understood what others need, she must help them satisfy those needs. Part of her social role as caregiver and nurturer of others involves putting her own needs second. Yet her needs do not remain merely secondary but often become hidden, for she herself does not have an emotional caregiver to turn to. There is an imbalance in the giving. *A woman then carries deep feelings of neediness* (1983, p. 9).

Again, the result is invisibility combined with serious emotional deprivation.

## Feminist theory

In feminist psychotherapeutic literature, it is generally agreed that severe anxiety in women begins with the oppressive sex-role conditioning of girls in society. Iris Fodor, writing in 1974 about 'The Phobic Syndrome in Women', contends that agoraphobia develops out of a woman's felt need to repress her desire for independence. As a girl, she learnt 'fearfulness and dependency' (Fodor 1974, p. 133), and while marriage is supposed to provide the haven she needs in adulthood, a woman often develops a trapped feeling in marriage. She wants to be independent but is afraid, and keeps her feelings bottled up inside herself till they eventually find expression in agoraphobia (1974, p. 133).

Joanna Rohrbaugh is another feminist writer who paints the same kind of picture. Girls are usually depicted in school text-books and in the popular media, she says, 'as helpless, incompetent, and fearful children who rely on boys, while boys master fear by contrasting themselves to girls and feeling good about their male superiority' (Rohrbaugh 1979, p. 419). In marriage, a woman who has learnt the female role well and knows the importance of pleasing her husband, often also feels anger and resentment toward him and toward the role she is expected to play, but is afraid to express her feelings directly. Under these circumstances, agoraphobia often develops. According to

Rohrbaugh, 'an agoraphobic woman simultaneously wishes for and fears . . . independence and assertiveness' (1979, p. 420). In summary, severe anxiety conditions often develop in women who: always try to please; feel trapped in their dependence and helplessness; wish for and fear independence and assertiveness; and are especially loath to express anger, preferring to deny it or block it out (1979, pp. 419–422).

Again, the contention that neurotic conditions in women are the result of the oppressive sex-role conditioning of girls and women in society is supported by Luise Eichenbaum and Suzie Orbach:

> The social requirements of deference, submission, and passivity generate many complicated feelings. Often women do not feel complete, substantial, or good within themselves. They feel afraid of their emotional needs, their insecurities and dependencies; they are fearful and guilty about their sexuality and their strivings for independence, nurturance, and power. The social requirements of patriarchy surround a girl from the moment of her birth (Eichenbaum & Orbach 1983, pp. 38–9).

Boys in patriarchal societies are raised with the expectation that there will always be someone to look after them and attend to them—first their mothers, grandmothers and sisters, then their wives, secretaries and daughters. Girls, on the other hand, are raised with the expectation that they will be the ones 'to provide the looking after and attending' (1983, p. 39). The result for women of such conditioning is that they *do* spend most of their lives looking after the physical and emotional needs of husbands, children, grandchildren, aging parents, and so on, while at the same time feeling guilty about their own deep-felt need for nurturing.

### A mother's role in the socialisation of daughters

The irony is that the person whose task it is to make sure a girl learns this caring, self-effacing, emotionally depriving role as well as possible is her mother. This presents a real dilemma for a mother who has come to realise the injustice of a situation that demands she be there always to respond to the needs of others, while no-one feels any compulsion to be there for her.

To illustrate the contrast, the following is an important example. The experience of many women is that when a man wants to talk over a problem, the woman is expected to give undivided attention for as long as he wants to talk. When the woman has a problem, the best she can expect is his half-hearted attention, and then only if she makes her complaint as brief as possible. The result, needless to say, is that when he unburdens himself to her he feels better and is able to get on with his life, but her attempt at unburdening herself to him leaves her feeling worse. She feels like a nuisance. She feels guilty for taking up his time. She feels agitated that her problem is no closer to being resolved. She blames herself for being so needy, and resolves to try harder in the future to keep her neediness to herself. His self-esteem is bolstered because of having been listened to, while her self-esteem receives another battering as, once again, it is confirmed for her that she is not worth listening to.

It is no wonder that a mother whose task it is to teach her daughters the female role 'is full of contradictory feelings, some conscious and some not' (1983, p. 42). The conflict for a mother is clear:

> On the one hand she hopes for a fuller and less restricted life for her daughter, while on the other she is fearful for a daughter who does not learn the essential feminine characteristics of restraining her own needs and desires and curbing her moves toward independence (1983, p. 42).

Because of a mother's own experience of emotional deprivation, she is careful not to set up false expectations for her daughter. At times she is impatient with and disapproving of her daughter for expressing her emotional needs and wanting more than she is going to get out of life. Slowly, and ever so subtly, girls are taught not to be emotionally dependent and not to expect to receive the emotional care and attention they might want.

While it is known that freedom of expression is important for mental health and happiness, mothers nevertheless find it necessary in bringing up their daughters to encourage them to *limit* their need to express their feelings of dissatisfaction and disappointment and anger, to *limit* their desires for emotional nurturing, and to *limit* their strivings toward independence (1983, pp. 42–3).

Consequently, girls grow up with strong admonitions to repress their feelings:

- Don't expect too much and you won't be disappointed.
- Don't express negative feelings because nobody wants to know.
- It doesn't matter how you really feel, so long as you smile.

### The need for empathy

Again the question arises: If it is true that most girls grow up with such unhealthy admonitions to repress their feelings, and if such repression (emotional deprivation) is a cause of severe anxiety, how is it that there are not more women who are agoraphobics or anxiety-sufferers? The answer lies in the fact that most mothers, even though they do assist society in the emotional deprivation of girls, are still able to empathise with their daughters' dissatisfaction. At some level, there develops between them an unconscious understanding that emotional deprivation is to be accepted as a normal part of life. It is this understanding, or bonding, which helps a girl to feel less alone and less guilty about her negative feelings.

### When there is no empathy

Some mothers, however, cannot bring themselves to empathise with their daughters' negative feelings—because of the unconscious fear that to do so might bring to the surface the mother's own desperate feelings of deprivation and resentment and anger, feelings she has struggled hard to ignore for many years. These mothers empathise only with their daughters' positive or happy feelings. When a girl receives empathy in relation to her positive feelings, but no response, no empathy in relation to expressions of so-called 'negative' feelings (anger, resentment, disappointment, sadness and so on), she does not develop the capacity 'to know that upsetting experiences can be gone through and tolerated' (1983, p. 162). She does not learn to accept negative feelings as a normal part of life, and consequently she lives in a state of emotional fragility. 'Her psychic structure is fragile ... She does not have the capacity to reassure herself or soothe herself. When she is flooded by bad feelings, her already fragile self almost seems to dissolve psychically' (1983, p. 162).

The absence of the ability to empathise with oneself leaves a woman with no option but to develop a way of hiding her negative feelings from herself. It is when her ability to hide her negative feelings from herself breaks down, that severe anxiety begins. Eichenbaum and Orbach talk about this breaking down in terms of 'the loss of critical elements in one's emotional security.' They go on to say:

> Such a loss . . . creates a situation of internal collapse. If a woman's relationships have been providing her sense of security, a significant loss destroys her illusory sense of well-being and throws her into a state of being with herself and her 'bad' internal relations (1983, p. 161).

In summary, feminist theory about the cause of severe anxiety in women leaves no doubt that it begins with the oppressive sex-role conditioning of girls in patriarchal society. Fathers contribute to this oppression when they expect their daughters to avoid negative expressions of feelings at all times and present themselves always as pleasant, helpful, cute, smiling, caring members of society. Mothers and daughters alike are victims of emotional deprivation. Out of a mother's own experience of deprivation, she teaches her daughter not to expect too much in terms of emotional nurturing. At the same time as she teaches her daughter how to limit her own needs, a mutual understanding (an empathy) develops between them which helps the girl feel less alone. It is when a mother, as a result of her own emotional deprivation, is *not* able to empathise with her daughter's negative feelings that the conditions are set for the development of severe anxiety.

## Women's experience of emotional deprivation

Taking the focus away from anxiety-sufferers in particular and looking in a more general way at emotional deprivation as it affects all women, it is not difficult to see that the most obvious area of emotional deprivation in our society is that of women in their relationships with men. Women are deprived in their relationships with men in at least four ways. In the first instance, *men rarely talk to women about how they feel*, and consequently women live day after day, week after week, year after year, wondering how the man they live with or work with is feeling, wondering in fact, if he feels anything at all. Even when a woman asks a man about his feelings, she rarely gets a satisfying response.

In Shere Hite's research (1987), she asked the women in her study a series of questions about 'men's emotional withholding and distancing' demonstrated by their 'reluctance to talk about personal thoughts and feelings.' The following are samples of the responses she received:

- His refusal to really share himself with me is a problem. I would like him to be more spontaneous, to talk deeply about his feelings, fears, or whatever. His ego doesn't permit it. I've yearned for sharing, but only get it with other friends. It could be better if he'd be more of a companion, talk more, have a sense of humor . . .

- He closes me off from him when he most needs support. Sometimes I feel like an outsider looking in.

- I would like for us to be able to say what is on our minds. My clue that something is bothering him is when he grinds his teeth when he sleeps.

- He's often silent for hours while we are alone, which gets on my nerves. I would like him to talk more about feelings—reactions—problems—but he's just not interested . . . he will only talk to me if he sees I'm desperate and I start to cry . . .

- If I could change one thing—it would be to get him to be more expressive of his emotions, his wants, needs. I most

129

criticize him for not telling me what he wants or how he feels. He denies he feels things when his non-verbals indicate he does feel them. I guess showing him true things, trying to get him to talk, is another service I am providing (1987, pp. 6, 21).

Second, *men rarely attempt to anticipate how women might be feeling.* Women, as mentioned before, are expected to have emotional antennae, to anticipate what others need and do everything in their power to help satisfy those needs. Men, on the other hand, have no such antennae, and consequently, the needs of women go largely unnoticed and unfulfilled.

- I cried out of frustration in my relationship with my husband when I repeatedly was unable to get him to respond to my emotional needs. After a few years, I was very depressed, everything felt like alienation, and the future looked like a black void. It was horrible.

- When I was raising four small children I felt very isolated. My husband had no idea of my loneliness because he was so engrossed in his work. We had little in-depth communication, which resulted in terrible loneliness . . . (1987, p. 24).

During those times in a woman's life when she most needs emotional support, some men seem automatically to develop even greater needs, so that their needs outweigh those of their partner. The result is that more and more is demanded of the woman while her partner remains totally oblivious to her needs. A common example is that which often occurs following the birth of a baby. A respondent in Cline and Spender's research described her experience as follows:

I got a dreadful shock when Sharon was born . . . I was just so pleased with her. It took me days to work out why my husband wasn't pleased. Why he was so upset. He was jealous. I know now. I was giving all my attention to the baby—and what about him? So I had to start making an extra effort with him. The doctor said it was normal. Happens

to everybody. Said just make him feel he's still the most
important person in your life. That's what I do now . . . (Cline
& Spender 1987, p. 166).

That same example could be used to illustrate the third way
women are emotionally deprived, and that is, *women's feelings are
often ignored.* If a woman's feelings are not expressed, they are
simply not noticed, but also, when they are expressed, they are
often not heard.

A seminar held a year or so ago on the subject of 'Communication between women and men' was attended by twelve women
and eleven men. At one point in the discussion, a male partici-
pant turned to the facilitator and said earnestly: 'Why don't
women tell us what they want? All men hear these days is that
women aren't happy in their relationships. If they would just tell
us what they want, we'd be able to do something about it.'

One of the women responded by saying: 'I can only speak for
myself, but all I want is for a man to listen to me sometimes. He
doesn't have to agree with me—just listen. I want him to listen
to what I say and care about how I feel.' All around the group
women were nodding in agreement. The man then turned back
to the facilitator and said: 'They never tell us what they want.
How can we be expected to change if they don't tell us?'

The women in the group were stunned! It was as if a time-
lapse had occurred. What the man said the second time he spoke
followed on immediately from his first speech, *as if nothing had
occurred in between!* What the woman said, as well as the response
of all the other women who were nodding and saying 'Yes', had
simply not registered with him. He had not heard it. This example represents a very common experience in women's lives, and a
very annoying one. When they say what they want and express
how they feel, they are simply not heard. They are ignored.

A fourth factor in women's emotional deprivation is the fact
that *women's emotions are rarely accepted at face value.* They are either
evaluated or trivialised. Common evaluative responses to
women's feelings are:

- You're too angry/too excitable/too silly/too impulsive.

- You cry too much.

131

- Your crying is just a ploy to manipulate me.

- You've got nothing to be unhappy about. You should be happy.

Another example from Shere Hite's research: 'When I try to tell him my feelings or needs, he always says it's bullshit' (1987, p. 6).

When a woman's feelings are evaluated in these ways, she is given to understand that she does not have the 'right' to feel the way she does, and that if she really does feel like that, there must be something wrong with her.

Common examples of the trivialising of women's feelings are:

- You're cute when you're angry.

- You don't really mean that.

- You can't still be feeling depressed.

- You're making too much of it.

- You're just being silly.

Such trivialising responses are designed to make a woman feel embarrassed about the intensity of her feelings, and again, she is given a strong message that there is something wrong with her for feeling the way she does.

Incidents from the lives of the women who wrote their stories for the purposes of this book provide more everyday examples of emotional deprivation. It is not surprising that most of their stories on this topic are about *emotional deprivation in relationships with male partners*:

> After 28 years of marriage, if I was asked to give a word picture of my husband, I would find it very difficult. Oh, I could describe his looks all right, but I just don't know much about him. I don't know how he feels about anything really. I don't know what colour he likes, who he likes, what he dislikes.
>
> I know what he tolerates, but that is only from practical experience. He has never shown himself to me.

We were lying in bed together. He was snoring. I was thinking, restless, fuming. He had been two hours late coming home and I was consumed with worry for his safety. I had walked up and down. I had rung the theatre where he was working. I had imagined every possible scenario.

I was so relieved when he walked in. I went straight to him to hold him, to kiss him. 'Where have you been? I've been frantic', although I already knew from the smell of alcohol on his breath. 'Just having a few drinks. What's the matter?'

I told him of my concerns, my worries and then my anger. Where did I fit into this? Don't I have a right to be thought of? I would never be this uncaring and would certainly never treat him like this. We loved each other. He knew that I didn't want to own him. We gave each other a lot of freedom but I thought we also gave each other courtesy.

The worst is that he can sleep like a baby while I lie here, unresolved, feeling uncared for, fuming, fighting the urge to wake him up and scream at him and be 'irrational'. I know I will have to get over it by myself.

I had had news from home that a family friend had died. She was still a young woman with three small children who had suffered from a terminal illness for some years. This woman, somewhat older than I was, had made an impression during my teenage years.

She called to see me prior to my departure for an overseas holiday with a small farewell gift, and already symptoms of her illness were apparent. It was not long afterwards that my mother wrote to say she had died.

I felt quite emotional, although I hadn't had much contact with her for some time. My partner reacted to my distress with impatience, saying he hadn't heard me mention her before and it wasn't as if she was a close friend, so why was I suddenly getting sentimental. He clearly regarded my emotions as inauthentic.

I said no more about it and stifled my tears. I found myself wondering if I was indeed being shallow and superficial in my reactions . . .

I had been in a relationship with Russell for more than a year and we had been living together for about six months. My mother was very ill and I was really upset. When I had been a teenager my mother had been diagnosed as having cancer, but she would not discuss her condition with me. It was all a big black secret and for a number of years I lived in fear that she would die and my sisters and I would be on our own with no money, or sent to an orphanage, or made to live with relatives we didn't know.

So, when Mum was sick again and wouldn't say what was wrong with her, and I was living in a different city to her, I got upset and was lying in bed having a cry when Russell came in to go to bed. He said, 'I suppose you're like this because of your mother', and I sniffed a little 'yes'. He then said, 'You know this is just over the top, don't you? Why don't you just get yourself together? If this is how you react when your mother gets a bit crook, you're going to be just impossible to cope with when she dies. If we're still together then, I don't know if I'll be able to cope.'

Where was the warm support and comfort I had expected? Why was I being criticised for expressing my very real pain? Why had he denied my need to be comforted, and instead pointed out how he was going to be inconvenienced by my grief sometime in the future? I felt betrayed, unloved and hurt. I felt a cold dagger in my heart.

It had been more than a year since my father's death, an event and loss which even by that time caused me great angst and remorse. Although my husband, John, had initially been very comforting, my need to grieve, to speak of Dad's illness and death was still paramount.

We were driving home from work and, although I do not recall the trigger, once again I began to speak of the guilt I felt at the things I had done and at the things I had failed to do. Exasperated, John turned to me and said, 'I am sick of listening to this! There's nothing I can do.' We drove the remaining 10 kms in silence, I feeling heart-struck that my husband of thirteen years hadn't realised that *listening* was exactly what he could do, and realising that his peace was more important to him than my pain.

Hurt and chagrined, I vowed that I would never again risk speaking to him with such freedom and intimacy.

I don't generally consider I have a good memory for events and happenings in my past. However, I have a clear picture of an incident that happened early in my married life, which on looking back now and thinking about it, I realise had quite an impact on me.

I was a young mother with a daughter of 23 months and a baby son of five weeks when I developed a painful abscess on my right breast. I was told by my doctor I would have to give up breast-feeding immediately, and was warned by him—in response to my plea—that I couldn't continue feeding my baby in the other breast as both would then become infected.

I was quite distraught by this news. I enjoyed breast-feeding and was quite convinced of the health benefits for the baby. I had breast-fed my daughter to nine months and had hoped to do the same for my son. At the first 6 o'clock feed that night, I mixed up the formula and gave it to the baby. I remember going for a shower and already my breasts were hard and swollen with the milk inside them. I can't recall the 10 o'clock and 2 am feeds, but by the 6 am feed the next morning, the baby's stomach was so upset by the complete and sudden change of milk that he vomited all over me.

I was not normally a mother who couldn't cope. I was rearing my two children without family support and with a husband whose professional and social life kept him away from the home from 8 o'clock in the morning until 7 o'clock at night. With only one car in the family, I found motherhood a very isolating and, at times, depressing experience, but one I believed I was coping with capably.

This particular morning, though, I knew I absolutely had to have my husband there to support me that day. My abscess was painful, my breasts were swollen and sore, my baby was vomiting on the new milk, I was psychologically distressed by all this, and I had a young daughter to mind. I begged him to stay with me that day, but he had a plane to catch—he was going to a meeting in Brisbane and just couldn't stay—so he left.

It was a turning point. I was being told that it was my job and mine alone, under every and all circumstances, to be responsible for the children, and that no matter what needs I may have, his needs were greater. At the time, I believed and accepted that. Now I wonder. Why couldn't the meeting have been put off? Couldn't he have phoned and said he had a sick wife and child and couldn't make it that day?

Was that meeting of men so important that he *had* to go?

One story was about *emotional deprivation in a lesbian relationship:*

Over the time we had known each other, we seemed to be growing closer every day. We spent all our spare time together, talking, laughing, enjoying each other's company. It seemed inevitable that we would one day be lovers—and we were. It happened quite naturally one Saturday afternoon, and it was lovely. I felt closer to her than I had ever been to anyone, and I think she felt the same. Later that evening, she left my place and went home, with my promise that I would phone her the next morning.

I woke early Sunday morning full of anticipation and excitement and love. I waited till a respectable hour and then made my phonecall.

She answered, and as I spoke something seemed to go wrong with the phone. I rang again. This time, there was an engaged signal. I waited and rang again, and again, and again. It was busy for a long time. Later, when I tried again, the phone rang, but no one answered. I was puzzled, but told myself there could be many explanations.

As the day wore on, the awful truth began to dawn on me . . . No, it couldn't be! Into the evening, I kept phoning. Then, at last, someone answered. I asked for my friend. The woman's voice (her mother, I think) said 'She's not available'. I said 'Could you tell me when she will be available?' The voice said 'She isn't going to be available'.

From that time on, I never saw or heard from her again . . .

One woman wrote about *her mother's emotional deprivation* and its effect on her:

It's hard to think of a single incident related to emotional deprivation. It seems as if it's been a permanent state going back to the beginning. My mother: a recently widowed woman at my birth, running a newspaper single-handed in a small male-dominated town, with four children (aged 0–16), no car, and we lived two miles out of town, and absolutely no support.

How could she possibly satisfy the emotional needs of her children? I feel horrified when I begin to inspect the depths of her emotional deprivation. So it's like a constant theme. There's never been enough love and support. (Isn't this true for most women? Who nurtures the nurturers?)

It is improving now. I've learnt how to recognise and state my needs, and successfully negotiate their fulfilment. But it's always a bit of a struggle (I hate having to *ask*)—never quite enough to go around.

Then, there was a story about *emotional deprivation by a friend*:

My current boyfriend had decided suddenly to end our relationship. I felt shredded, totally let down, and in need of lots of TLC. [tender-loving-care]. Three girlfriends came to visit on Saturday afternoon. One of them had been in a bad relationship for some time and I had tried to be supportive to her over the past few months.

She arrived, and after asking how I was, to which I replied 'Lousy', she commenced to go on and on about the trouble she was having and how what I was going through was similar to her problems. Perhaps it was, but it left me feeling really disappointed, misunderstood and short-changed. Why couldn't she let *me* be the focus for just a short time?

One woman told of her feelings of *emotional deprivation during a job interview*. The attitude of the interviewer was so cold and cruel that she was left feeling 'destroyed':

I'd managed to keep my nervousness about this interview under control by reassuring myself that the man I'd be facing was experienced in interpersonal communications. I believed I could be honest in expressing what I thought and felt, for if he had to let me know I was unsuccessful in my application, it wouldn't be at the cost of my self-respect.

My spirits sank when I found myself sitting across from him separated by what seemed to me at the time like the most enormous desk I'd ever seen. It's size, though, was just an illusion as, I found, was my trust in this man.

After the question and answer routine in which I had allowed my honest self-representation to take its course, he proceeded to lecture me about the danger of emotional involvement with issues. He made no attempt to disguise the coldness of his voice and manner. He literally looked down his nose at me as he picked my every response apart.

I flamed with embarrassment and felt my throat tighten. It was as well I wasn't expected to respond. The words wouldn't have formed. I could hardly wait to escape that place and find the safety of the car outside, where my best friend waited for me. I cried and raged and, through my tears, could only repeat over and over, 'He's destroyed me'.

Finally, a woman told of *emotional deprivation in relation to the church*. When she most needed the comfort of the church, she received rejection and condemnation:

My daughter often comments 'That is just a social construct' to nearly any accepted practice I care to mention. By that she means, that any beliefs and rituals practised in any society are constructed by that society. They are not necessarily right or the only way to do something. This seems to me to be an apt description of religion.

I was once very much influenced and controlled by the religion I inherited from my parents. I relied on the priests to give me the guidance, approval, forgiveness and acceptance needed to live my life the best way I possibly could.

When I was 22, I became pregnant with my second child. Because of weakness in the wall of the placenta, I spent three months in bed—most of this time in hospital. My physical well-being and that of my baby depended on the professional care of the doctors and nurses. I leaned heavily on my husband and religion for emotional support.

Despite all the medical care available, my baby was born prematurely and we were advised to prepare for his death. I was completely devastated by the emptiness and loneliness I experienced after his death, and desperately needed emotional support from those closest to me.

The day after my baby died, the hospital priest visited me. He seemed to care as I had hoped he would and asked me if I would like to take communion. I explained I couldn't because I hadn't been to confession for a long time. He asked why, and I told him that between the births of the children I had been taking an oral contraceptive. He looked at me and said that the baby's death was God's punishment to me for having sinned against him. He then left.

Although he was just one man, I had been taught that priests were God's representatives on earth and so I believed what he said was true.

Also, our parish priest refused to attend the burial of our baby because we couldn't afford to pay him. I felt God had deserted me!

Again, it must be said that the value of these real-life stories, in the context of this book, lies in the fact that they serve as reminders of how prevalent such incidents are in women's lives, and that it only takes one such incident to trigger an anxiety attack in women who already have the preconditions for the development of severe anxiety.

It is important, therefore, that women in general, and anxiety-sufferers in particular, find ways of counteracting the effects of the emotional deprivation built into women's role. The first step a woman must take, after finding the courage to admit to herself that adequate emotional support is not available to her in her present relationships, is to talk to those closest to her and give them a chance to change their attitude toward her. If they are not interested in responding to her needs, however, the next step is for her to seek out other people who will provide the emotional support she needs. More and more women these days are asking for, and receiving, strong emotional support from other women—friends, sisters, mothers, daughters, as well as Women's Centres and other women's groups. In these ways, the deprivation caused by lack of emotional support is being eased.

## Two courses of action

This chapter and the two preceding it have examined the issues of women's powerlessness, invisibility and emotional deprivation as possible causes of severe anxiety in individual women. On the basis of this analysis, two tasks present themselves as important courses of action for anxiety-sufferers—once they have freed themselves from the trauma of their condition by the method set out in chapter 6.

One task is to *analyse your own particular situation, in light of the theories outlined above, with a view to achieving a greater understanding of the cause of your own condition.* Allow yourself to delve into thoughts of your past in an attempt to uncover the dynamics that may have contributed to the development in you of the predisposition to severe anxiety. What were the dynamics of your childhood relationship with your parents and siblings? Were you a 'pampered' child? . . . an emotionally neglected child? . . . a sexually abused child? . . . an emotionally abused child? How did you defend yourself against childhood feelings of powerlessness? How did you respond, in childhood and adulthood, to experiences of 'nonbeing'? Were you encouraged to express your negative feelings or ignore them?

The other task is to *develop an awareness of how this age of anxiety for women is affecting you personally.* In other words, *raise your consciousness about those times in your daily life when you experience powerlessness, invisibility and emotional deprivation, and work at counteracting the effects of those experiences.*

Experiences of powerlessness can be reversed by deliberately claiming your own personal power, by learning to become more confident and assertive, and by allowing yourself to express anger whenever you feel it; experiences of invisibility can be reversed by strengthening your self-esteem and self-affirmation; and experiences of emotional deprivation can be reversed by avoiding those people who drain you, and deliberately seeking out people (especially women) who will freely give you the emotional support you need.

# 6

# A treatment method that works

The method of treatment outlined in the following pages is actually a very simple process. Once an anxiety-sufferer begins to trust the treatment process, she is well on the way to being cured. For some, however, this first requirement of trusting the process is the most difficult one of all in their journey towards achieving a cure, because the central element in this treatment seems to go against everything they ever believed about their condition.

Most anxiety-sufferers believe that their anxiety problems exist because they are not exercising enough control over their emotions. It is a sign of their weakness, they think, and all they really need to do is develop enough strength of character to be able to control themselves properly and their anxiety would vanish. Control becomes the overwhelming focus of an anxiety-sufferer's attention, and loss of control is the thing she fears more than anything else. It is understandable, then, that a treatment method which begins with the imperative: *the first thing an anxiety-sufferer must do is stop trying to control her anxiety*, would seem to make little sense. This, nevertheless, is the central element or the basic requirement of the following treatment. *If you, the anxiety-sufferer, want your anxiety to go away, you must stop trying to make it go away. If you want your anxiety to be brought under control, you must stop trying to bring it under control. Just let it be.*

The treatment outlined in this chapter has been developed in line with a Japanese cognitive-behavioural therapy called Morita therapy. It is 'cognitive' and 'behavioural' in that it encourages the anxiety-sufferer to focus attention on her *thinking* and *behaviour* rather than her feelings. It will be helpful first to investigate Morita therapy as an introduction to the treatment plan itself, in order to see how the method was developed and the assumptions on which it is based.

## Morita therapy

Morita therapy, developed in Japan around 1920 by Professor Shoma Morita, is unique in that it was designed for one type of client only—the 'nervous' client, or in Japanese, the *shinkeishitsu* client: people suffering from anxiety-related conditions such as hypochondria, anxiety neurosis (the condition referred to here as 'severe anxiety'), phobias, obsessive-compulsive neurosis, and psychosomatic conditions.

Shoma Morita himself had what he called a *shinkeishitsu* disposition. He suffered from severe anxiety. He recalled having had an extreme fear of death from around age nine, which came and went through his teenage years. When he was nineteen, he had his first anxiety attack. Puzzled and devastated by his condition, he decided to study psychiatry at Tokyo University where he began to experiment with various methods of treatment, out of which he developed the therapy which has come to be called Morita therapy.

In the writings of Morita therapists most of the attention is given to treatment rather than cause, consistent with their belief that the activity that keeps anxiety alive in a person is that person's preoccupation with it, and that any enquiry into how one's anxiety started is in fact an opportunity to continue one's self-preoccupation. Only in the initial therapy session is a person encouraged to speculate on the possible cause of her condition, but after the first session such speculation is discouraged so that it does not become a hindrance to successful treatment.

Regarding cause, Morita therapists do say that the *shinkeishitsu* condition is caused by a predisposition to 'nervousness and hyper-sensitivity' combined with a learned pattern of 'anxious self-preoccupation', and while everybody has a predisposition to nervousness and hypersensitivity (which, in simple language, means 'normal anxiety'), not everybody learns the habit of anxious self-preoccupation. It is those who develop the habit of anxious self-preoccupation who will suffer from severe (neurotic) anxiety (Ishiyama 1986a, p. 376).

A look at the assumptions on which Morita therapy is based will help anxiety-sufferers see the significance of the therapy itself, and also help in applying the treatment outlined in the following pages to their own experience.

### Normal anxiety is a normal part of life

Morita therapists draw attention to 'the normal and inevitable nature of fears and anxieties' (Ishiyama 1986b, p. 558). As mentioned above, people who suffer with severe anxiety start off with the same fears and anxieties as everyone else—normal, acceptable, manageable anxiety about death, illness, injury, helplessness, loneliness, and so on. Such anxiety is normal anxiety, and is a normal part of everyone's life.

### Preoccupation with normal anxiety causes neurotic anxiety

While most people are able to incorporate normal anxiety into their lives and get on with living, something happens in some people to cause an excessive preoccupation with normal anxiety. This preoccupation then causes it to become neurotic or severe anxiety.

### Anxiety, both normal and neurotic, must be accepted

Anything that forms part of one's life must be accepted and incorporated into the whole. If one attempts to ignore or reject any part of one's self, then the integrity of the whole is damaged. (The need to accept one's anxiety is the first step in the treatment itself, and will be discussed in more detail in the following pages.)

### Anxiety will lessen spontaneously if left alone

Anxiety will lessen spontaneously 'if left unaggravated by conscious manipulation' (Ishiyama 1986a, p. 377). In other words,
your anxiety will go away of its own accord if you just stop
giving it attention. The thing that keeps anxiety alive is one's
constant thinking about it.

### Neurotic anxiety must be reinterpreted

The usual interpretation of severe anxiety is that it comes from a
fear of death, and that includes symbolic death (such as illness,
loneliness, emptiness, meaninglessness, nothingness), as well as
real death (physical death). Morita therapists see such fear of
death as an indication of a desire for life. They are two sides of
the one coin. A fear of illness is, in fact, a desire for health; fear
of emptiness is a desire for fullness of life; fear of meaninglessness is a desire for meaningfulness; and so on. Anxiety-sufferers
must take hold of their fear of physical and symbolic death, and
reinterpret it in their own minds as a desire for life.

### Behaviour is more important than emotion

Instead of focusing on her emotion, the anxious person must
reduce her unproductive self-preoccupation by applying her nervous energy to practical activities for productive purposes. What
a person *does* must be seen by her as more important than what
she *feels*.

# THE TREATMENT

The following treatment method has been developed in line
with the above assumptions about anxiety, and it is a method that
enjoys great success. Studies into the outcome of Morita treatment reveal an 80 to 90 per cent success rate, and success in
those studies meant either complete cure or major improvement.

Anyone who has read *Self Help for your Nerves* (Weekes 1962)
will see the similarities between the treatment developed by Dr
Weekes and that developed by Dr Morita. Claire Weekes

summarises her treatment by using four simple principles:

*Facing* Whenever anxiety comes upon you, she says, you must not run away from it but face it. 'Stop regarding it as some monster trying to possess you' (p. 22). Breathe slowly and deeply and go with it.

*Accepting* Instead of fighting it, *'be prepared to accept and live with it for the time being,'* because by so doing, you will 'break the fear-adrenalin-fear cycle . . .' She says the churning in your stomach 'will eventually leave you if you are prepared to let time pass and not anxiously watch the churning during its passing' (p. 22).

*Floating* When your anxiety is high and you are paralysed with fear about going to the shop or walking up a flight of stairs, instead of forcing yourself, you should try to imagine you are 'floating'. Imagine yourself on a cloud, floating down the street to the shop or floating up the stairs. Dr Weekes encouraged her patients to say to themselves: 'Float and you can do it. Float past fear' (p. 30).

*Letting time pass* As you learn the art of floating, you must also be patient. Allow your anxiety to leave you in its own time. *'You don't have to strive for relaxation,'* she says. 'You have *to wait for it'* (p. 32).

The positive statement made by Dr Weekes at the beginning of her book is true also of the Morita treatment process to follow. She says: 'The advice given here will definitely cure you, if you follow it' (Weekes 1962, p. 1).

It must be said, however, that there are occasions when these treatments are not successful, and those occasions are when a person's anxiety condition is complicated by a serious mental illness, by chronic depression, or by a problem-relationship where one or both partners need to keep the anxiety alive in order for the relationship to survive. The reason why it does not work on those occasions is that an important prerequisite for the success of the treatment is the anxiety-sufferer's commitment to the process, and those whose anxiety is complicated by any of the above usually lack the kind of commitment required.

Those who suffer from any kind of psychotic illness are advised to work (with a psychiatrist) toward the stabilising of your psychosis first before attempting to commit yourself to the Morita process. If you suffer with chronic depression, it is advisable to try to work through your depression first (with a psychotherapist or psychiatrist) so that you will then have the motivation to commit yourself to the following treatment process. A depressed person is an unmotivated person, or as Claire Weekes put it: '. . . depression and apathy rob their victim of the desire to recover' (p. 58). If you are in a relationship that seems to need your anxiety to give the relationship meaning, you will never be committed to getting rid of your anxiety until you work to change the dynamics of the relationship or make a decision to end it. Before attempting the following treatment process, you are advised to see a psychotherapist or a marriage counsellor with a view to getting your relationship sorted out first.

To those anxiety-sufferers who are among the 80 to 90 per cent who are free of such complications, I say with certainty that if you can believe the condition is curable, if you want to be cured, and if you follow the directives set out in the following treatment plan, *you will be cured*. It is important to note the word 'directives'. These are not suggestions or requests, but directives. Morita therapy is a directive therapy. You cannot enter into it half-heartedly. It demands a commitment from you that you will do whatever is necessary in order to effect your own cure.

## 1 Accept your anxiety

The decision to accept your anxiety in fact means you will stop rejecting it, stop trying to control or eliminate it, and stop seeing it as a personal weakness or mental abnormality. It means, instead of continuing to view it in a negative way, you have decided to develop a more positive attitude toward it.

To be able to accept your anxiety, you must be prepared to develop a new way of relating to it; develop an awareness of anxiety as an emotion; develop an understanding of the true meaning of acceptance; and acknowledge the connection between acceptance of your anxiety and self-acceptance.

### Develop a new way of relating to your anxiety

It is important to begin thinking about your anxiety in a more personal, intimate way. Realise your anxiety is *yours*. It is not some foreign thing that invades your life and renders you powerless. It has come from within you. It is you, and you must be prepared to claim it as your own.

Many anxiety-sufferers experience the idea of accepting their anxiety as abhorrent. They prefer to continue thinking about it as a passing thing, an aberration, something not really related to them that will disappear if they struggle with it hard enough. The sad truth is that it is the struggle that keeps the anxiety alive.

It is at this point in a therapy session, when the therapist talks to the anxiety-sufferer about the need to stop fighting against anxiety and just to accept it, that some people turn off. They spend the rest of the session trying to convince the therapist of the need to keep fighting, because to give up the fight, they say, is to run the risk of sinking totally under the weight of it, never to rise again. Some reject the idea of acceptance so much that they refuse to continue with therapy, and instead strengthen their resolve to fight it, but fighting it simply does not work.

If you have related to your anxiety as to an enemy, then you must change your way of relating to it. Instead of fighting against it, give in to it, surrender to it, and claim it as an interesting and acceptable part of who you are. Once you decide to give up the fight, you will experience the relief that comes from no longer having to be constantly prepared for battle. This new way of relating to your anxiety allows you to work with it rather than against it.

### Develop an awareness of anxiety as an emotion

The anxiety feelings you have, however severe, are simply feelings, and like all feelings (emotions) they are spontaneous. They cannot be brought on or stopped by an act of will. You cannot say: 'I think I'll feel happy now', and will yourself to be happy. Emotions come and go as they please, and the only thing to do with emotions is let them be.

When you are feeling happy, you might be able to will yourself to stop smiling or laughing, but you cannot will yourself to stop feeling happy. Similarly, when you are feeling anxious, you might be able to will yourself to stop shaking, but you cannot will yourself to stop feeling anxious. Feelings just are. They come and go of their own accord, so the most sensible thing to do is accept them.

Anger is an emotion many women have difficulty accepting, preferring to think of themselves as people who never get angry. What they do, then, when something happens that would normally cause a person to feel anger, is ignore or repress their feelings so that they can go on believing they are not angry. The fact that anger is not expressed, however, does not mean it has been resolved. It stays there, churning around inside the person, causing depression, anxiety, stress and so on, waiting for a chance to explode in some way. Anger that is not expressed, anger that is not accepted, does not go away.

If emotions are accepted and allowed to be, they will follow their own course, disappear when they are ready and cause you the least possible trouble. Anxiety is such an emotion.

### Develop an understanding of the true meaning of acceptance

First, acceptance of anxiety does not mean ignoring it or pretending it is not there. The advice an anxiety-sufferer often receives from those around her is: Just forget about it. Ignore it. Pretend it is not there.

It *is* there, however, and its existence must be recognised and accepted. The effort to ignore it usually only helps make other people feel better because on the surface things seem to have changed, but the anxiety-sufferer herself continues to be all too aware that nothing has really changed. Ignoring it involves an extreme act of the will which only serves to keep the anxiety alive, whereas accepting it brings peace and calm.

Second, acceptance of anxiety does not mean you have to like it or love it. It is not possible to love something that has caused such pain and disruption to your life, but this is the advice anxiety-sufferers are often given. So-called 'new age' thinking which encourages everyone to think positively about everything, calls upon people in pain to 'love' their pain. To people suffering from extreme anxiety, they suggest: 'love' your anxiety. It must be said that it is not necessary to attempt to love your anxiety because the truth is, you do not love it, and to say you do would be false.

It is probably closer to the truth to say you hate it, but even though that is more truthful, it is also not helpful. 'Love' and 'hate' are strong emotions, and it is important to try to take the emotion out of your relationship with your anxiety. To accept it is to say: 'I don't love it or hate it. It's in my life at the moment, and that's all right, but it will also be all right when it leaves me. Whatever my anxiety does, I accept it.'

Finally, acceptance of anxiety does not mean simply resigning oneself to it. Admittedly, acceptance often begins with an attitude of resignation, but it is important to move from that point to real acceptance. Resignation usually includes a degree of impatience with the situation of having to accept what one does not want to accept. It can also include feelings of indignation or bitterness or resentment. These kinds of feelings are natural as you resign yourself to accepting your anxiety condition, but it is important that your acceptance does not stop at the resignation stage, because it is only real acceptance that will allow you to stop fighting against your anxiety. Then, and only then, will it begin to subside.

### Acknowledge the connection between acceptance of your anxiety and self-acceptance

Many anxiety-sufferers refuse to accept their anxiety because they continue to hold on to the hope that they will one day revert to their old selves again, and the idea of accepting it sounds to them like a path of no return. The fact is, however, that once a person has experienced severe anxiety, it is not possible to go back to being a person who has not experienced severe anxiety. In that sense, you will never go back to being who you used to be. When you are free of your anxiety, rather than being as you were in your pre-anxiety days, you will be who you have become as a result of all of life's experiences since then, and that includes your experience of anxiety. Acceptance of anxiety is, in fact, an integral part of self-acceptance, and refusal to accept your anxiety is a refusal to accept yourself.

If you wait till you can feel better about yourself before accepting yourself, then you probably never will accept yourself. The secret of improving your self-esteem lies in a willingness to accept yourself unconditionally. Before an alcoholic can change her drinking behaviour, she has to begin by saying: 'I'm an alcoholic', and the reason why those words are so important is because the person is actually saying: 'I accept who I am. I am an alcoholic.' Many alcoholics speak of the relief they felt when they were finally able to admit the truth about themselves and accept their condition as an integral part of themselves.

Anxiety-sufferers, too, after months or years of feeling shame because of their condition, speak of the relief they felt when they were finally able to admit to themselves and to others: 'I'm an anxiety-sufferer.' Before any changes can take place, an anxiety-sufferer must allow herself to be fully aware of who she is. Such self-awareness is a prerequisite for self-acceptance, and self-acceptance leads to healing and growth.

## 2  Learn about your anxiety

Make it your business to become knowledgeable about anxiety so that you develop a thorough understanding of what is going on in you. Do not be satisfied any longer to flounder around in the dark, passively depending on a doctor or therapist who may or may not have any more knowledge of the condition than you do. It is your condition, so take it into your own hands. Read as much as you can find about it. Seek out seminars or lectures on the topic. Make sure you understand the difference between normal anxiety and neurotic (severe) anxiety. Become an 'expert' on the subject for your own sake, so that your condition is no longer something that is hidden from your understanding.

When something happens in your life that you are not able to control regardless of how hard you try, it leaves you confused and mystified, and has a devastating and debilitating effect on you. It takes away your confidence, lowers your self-esteem, drains you of any sense of power over your own life, and calls into question everything you have ever believed about the security of your own existence in the world. The experience of severe anxiety effects the anxiety-sufferer in these ways. Conversely, knowledge about the condition restores confidence, increases self-esteem, brings power, and gives a more comprehensive understanding of what life is really all about.

### Knowledge restores confidence

Most people have had the experience of walking into an already functioning group in the middle of a conversation, or arriving late to a class or committee meeting to find the others deep in discussion about something. In those situations it is difficult to find the confidence to join in the conversation or discussion because you have no knowledge of what has gone on before you arrived. Lack of knowledge causes lack of confidence, and it is not until you have listened for a while and your knowledge increases that you have the confidence to participate in the discussion. While lack of knowledge about your anxiety condition has undermined your confidence in yourself in the past, knowledge about the condition will restore your confidence.

### Knowledge increases self-esteem

Lack of knowledge about the condition means that an anxiety-sufferer goes through months or years of blaming herself. Self-disgust is a common feeling. She knows what she used to be like and what she is capable of, but because of these feelings she cannot control she is not able to be who she wants to be, and consequently there is a very real sense of alienation from herself. She feels that she does not know herself, and experiences herself as a stranger.

Blaming oneself, self-disgust, alienation from the self, all work together to bring one's self-esteem down to a very low level. Learning the truth about the condition—that severe anxiety is not caused by anything the sufferer has done or not done, that severe anxiety is not a sign of inherent weakness—

causes one's self-esteem to increase dramatically.

### Knowledge brings power

A sense of utter powerlessness is very real in anxiety-sufferers. They feel oppressed by this thing that came into their lives uninvited and refuses to leave no matter what they do to try to get rid of it.

An interesting way for an anxiety-sufferer to think of her experience is in terms of oppression because it then allows her to look at the way other groups have worked to liberate themselves from oppression, and adapt that to her own situation. (Such an analogy must not be taken too far, however, because there is a big difference between oppression by an outside oppressor and oppression experienced from within. In the area of the pursuit of knowledge, though, it can be very helpful.)

Various liberation movements have used the term 'consciousness raising' to describe what happens when an oppressed person or group of people attain knowledge about their situation. Paulo Freire wrote about the need for the peasant population of Brazil to pursue educational objectives, to learn to read and write, to seek to understand the oppression that kept them in a constant state of poverty and powerlessness. He saw that knowledge was the only chance they had for liberation (Freire 1972).

In Australia, there is evidence that Aboriginal Australians have also become aware in recent years of the power of knowledge. A decade or so ago Aboriginal parents began in earnest to encourage their children to take education seriously, to avail themselves of opportunities for tertiary education, to learn as much as they could, because they realised the power of knowledge to bring freedom from oppression. It is knowledge that can change powerlessness into a sense of real power.

Women, too, are being encouraged by the women's movement to seek knowledge, not only knowledge through formal education but also knowledge that comes when a woman is prepared to open up her eyes and seek the truth. Once a woman's consciousness is raised about the different ways she is oppressed both at a personal and social level she becomes dissatisfied, angry and determined to fight her oppression. The fight for her rights replaces her powerlessness with a sense of power. Knowledge helps oppressed people to see and believe that they no longer need be afraid of the oppressor. It allows an oppressed person to claim her own power.

The knowledge gained by an anxiety-sufferer about her hitherto mystifying condition helps her understand that her anxiety has only been able to oppress her because she has allowed it to have that kind of power over her. Now she sees that she has a choice, either to continue giving her power away and thereby continuing to feel oppressed, or to take back her power by accepting her anxiety, allowing it to be, and getting on with her life.

### Knowledge brings new understanding about human existence

The effort to learn about one's anxiety condition brings a new understanding not only about anxiety, but also about human existence. While it is natural for all thinking people to develop their own way of viewing the world and their own security patterns, anxiety-sufferers seem to view the world as an unsafe place and, therefore, go to extreme lengths sometimes to ensure a sense of security. Most anxiety conditions have a perfectionist component to them, which is the anxiety-sufferer's way of attempting to be in control of her own world.

The experience of severe anxiety takes away a person's sense of security and calls into question everything she ever thought about human existence that made her feel safe. All her efforts at control have not worked. As she learns about her condition, though, she begins to be able to accept that death is inevitable; that nonbeing is a part of being and cannot be avoided; that illness, loneliness, powerlessness, meaninglessness and so on, are just as much a part of life as health, belonging, power, and meaningfulness.

The gradual coming to terms with the uncontrollability of life allows the anxiety-sufferer to give up her need to be in control of her anxiety and simply accept it as something that is.

Where does one obtain this knowledge? How does one learn about severe anxiety? One very important thing to do is to *seek out reading material*. Many anxiety-sufferers do as Kate did when she found herself overwhelmed with symptoms for which she could find no explanation. She 'furtively searched out books and articles in libraries and bookshops' (see chapter 1). She could not bring herself to talk to anyone or to seek out knowledge openly because she felt so ashamed of what she perceived as her 'weakness'. Anxiety-sufferers are strongly advised to seek out reading material, not secretly, but *openly*. When you do that, however, it is important to take heed of the following words of warning.

First, not everything you will find to read on the subject will be helpful. This has been such a misunderstood condition through the years that some books and journal articles written on the subject have been either very negative about the prospects of cure, or simply unhelpful in that they suggest ways of handling anxiety that many anxiety-sufferers have already tried without success. Just keep sifting through the literature until you find material that is helpful to you (Weekes 1962; Meares 1967; Reynolds 1976, 1984; Ishiyama 1986a, 1986b).

A second warning is that as you read, you may be tempted to look for causes for each individual attack that you experience. Some people go so far as to keep a book handy which they go through each time they have an attack in a frantic search to explain what might have caused it this time. This is the wrong way to use reading material on the topic. There is no cause and no explanation for each individual attack, and to read for that purpose is not only a waste of energy, but is also counterproductive.

A third warning about reading is that when you read about the variety of anxiety symptoms that exist, and realise there are many you have not yourself experienced, you may find yourself actually producing those symptoms and making your anxiety worse, because that is what anxiety-sufferers tend to do. This is in line with the hypochondriachal element in severe anxiety, and is something you must always be aware of so that you can minimise it. If you find yourself experiencing difficulty swallowing, for example, and realise you read recently that that is sometimes a symptom of anxiety, just make sure you do not focus your attention on your swallowing. Tell yourself it is simply your anxiety playing tricks on you and refuse to give it any attention, and then this new symptom will disappear before it has had a chance to establish itself. Provided you heed these three warnings, reading about severe anxiety will be very helpful.

Another way to obtain knowledge about your condition is to *speak with a therapist or doctor who has some knowledge about severe anxiety*. Again a warning needs to be issued that not all therapists or doctors are well informed about this condition, and when looking for a professional person to speak with, you ought to keep searching till you find someone who is helpful. Reliable information about the particular strengths of therapists and doctors is usually available at Women's Health Centres and Women's Information and Referral Centres. If you phone one of these centres where you live or in your capital city and ask them to recommend appropriate professional people in your area, you will no doubt receive the information you need. Failing that, you should phone your State Government Health Department and ask to speak to the Women's Health Unit or a women's health advisor.

Finally, another way of gaining knowledge about the condition is to *talk with other anxiety-sufferers* who have had first-hand experience of what you are going through, especially those who have found a cure by following the kind of treatment process outlined in this chapter. If such people are available to you, they will be very helpful.

To illustrate the value of learning about the condition, the following example shows how, for some anxiety-sufferers, knowledge brings instant relief. Some time ago I began receiving phonecalls from a woman with whom I had had no contact for about ten years. We had been friends in our early years, but mobility and poor motivation for correspondence meant our contact dwindled to nothing over the years. The first phonecall after such a long period of silence was a pleasant surprise, but I could tell something was wrong. She sounded somewhat desperate. When I asked her how things were going for her, she said things like: 'I'm OK, I think. Just a bit mixed up.' The first phonecall was a brief one, but she rang two or three more times over the next two weeks, and I began to get a clearer picture of what was happening in her life. She had resigned from her job, was not able to drive her car anymore, felt frightened all the time, and was spending most of her time at home because she was too afraid to go out.

I asked her if she knew what was wrong, and she said: 'No. I've been to so many doctors over the last couple of years, it isn't funny. They've got me on tranquillisers, but they're not helping.' I asked her a few more questions, like: 'Do you have attacks of panic sometimes?', and then I began talking about some of the other symptoms of severe anxiety. She was amazed to hear me talking about things she had thought no-one else in the world had ever experienced. After a fairly lengthy conversation, she said she ought to go because of her ever-increasing phone bill. Before we ended the call, I told her about Claire Weekes' book (1962) and strongly suggested she try to get hold of it and read it.

A week later she phoned again and sounded like a different person. 'I can't believe how good I feel', she said. After that, there was no further contact for many months, until recently she phoned to say she was back at work and feeling really good.

## 3  Reinterpret your anxiety

One way of interpreting severe anxiety is that it indicates a fear of death and a fear of social and personal failure, and while that is certainly true, it is nevertheless only half the story.

The other half of the story, or the other side of the same coin, as Morita therapists would say, is that anxiety also indicates a desire for life and a desire to live one's life in a meaningful and successful way. The correct interpretation of anxiety, then, takes into account 'the complementary relationship between fears and desires' (Ishiyama 1986b, p. 557). An acute fear of death represents a strong desire for life, and an acute fear of social and personal failure represents a strong desire to live a meaningful and purposeful life.

Instead of anxiety-sufferers continuing to view their anxiety in a totally negative way, Morita therapy insists on a 'fundamental attitudinal change through a positive reinterpretation of anxiety . . .' (Ishiyama 1986a, p. 377). In other words, you must change your attitude to your anxiety by reinterpreting it, by seeing it no longer as something that fills you with feelings of dread and fear and helplessness, but rather as something that reminds you of your unusually strong desire for life, for health, and for productive and constructive living (Ishiyama 1986b, p. 559).

## 4  Stop indulging in anxious self-preoccupation

Self-awareness and self-acceptance are important factors in emotional and mental health, but 'anxious self-preoccupation is a dysfunctional mental state where attention is rigidly fixated upon anxious thoughts and feelings' (Ishiyama 1986a, p. 377) and must be avoided at all costs.

Anxiety-sufferers are highly sensitised to the least little change in themselves—their energy level ('I wonder what it means that I'm feeling so tired these days'); their emotions ('Why do I feel this way? I wonder if I'm going crazy'); their bodily functioning ('I know this giddy feeling I'm experiencing as I walk along means I'm going to faint'). When you are feeling anxious, it is important to accept your anxiety feelings and let them be there, but do not become preoccupied with them, because 'anxious self-preoccupation . . . aggravates anxiety . . .' (Ishiyama 1986a, p. 378).

Focusing on your anxiety only makes it worse, but focusing your attention somewhere else will cause the anxiety to disappear. 'Spontaneously emergent emotions including anxiety will disappear from the foreground of awareness eventually and spontaneously if left unaggravated by conscious manipulation' (Ishiyama 1986a, p. 377). In other words, stop focusing on your anxiety, stop trying to make it go away, because anxiety will disappear of its own accord if only you will stop being preoccupied with it. When anxiety or panic feelings come upon you, try to deal with what is happening at a cognitive rather than a feeling level. Tell yourself that your thoughts can be stronger than your feelings, and that you do not need to be overwhelmed by these anxiety feelings. Self-talk is important, so long as it is neither anxious, panicky self-talk nor harsh, repressive self-talk. Talk to yourself in a way that is gentle and accepting. 'I know what's happening, and it's all right. It's only my anxiety that's making me feel like I'm going to faint. I'll just keep walking along here toward the shop. Everything's all right. There's nothing to be concerned about . . . Now, what am I going to buy when I get to the shop?' (It may help to imagine that you are on a cloud, floating to the shop) . . . Having acknowledged and accepted your anxiety and then focused your attention on your shopping list, you will find that your anxiety will have subsided by the time you arrive at the shop.

The amazing thing is that you only need to do this once to experience the 'miracle' of your anxiety spontaneously disappearing, and this one experience will strengthen you to respond again and again in this same way. Before long your anxiety will have lost its power to control and defeat you, and you will once again be in control of your own life.

## 5  Focus on actions (behaviour) rather than feelings

In the above example, the anxiety-sufferer used self-talk to take her attention off her feelings and make herself focus on the task at hand. This is an example of what is required in Morita therapy, where clients are told to 'persevere through anxious moments and shift their attention to immediate tasks and practical purposes' (Ishiyama 1986a, p. 379).

There are, in fact, two techniques an anxiety-sufferer may use, both of which call upon her to 'persevere through anxious moments'. One involves focusing on practical action and the other involves focusing on her own physical (not emotional) sensations.

### Focus on practical action

When an anxiety-sufferer is able to immerse herself in a practical and productive task in the midst of her anxiety, the anxiety feelings disappear. Many anxiety-sufferers make the mistake of waiting till their anxiety subsides before doing something they need to do, with the result that their anxiety increases and the task is often left undone. It is very important to persevere with everyday tasks and realise that even though you would like to be able to do those tasks without anxiety, you can do them just as well with anxiety. The point is that you must focus on action, you must do the tasks, regardless of how your anxiety level is at the time.

A teacher who is overcome with fear about walking up the stairs to her classroom to begin the day's teaching would like to be able to climb the stairs without anxiety, but if her anxiety is present she must climb the stairs anyway, because the important focus is the task of climbing the stairs in order to teach her class, and the task has to be done.

A mother who is fearful about giving her child some medicine prescribed by the doctor because her anxiety is causing her to imagine she may do harm to the child, must give the child the medicine anyway because the task has to be done. If you know in your head it is the correct action to take, do it however fearfully. Focus on the action that needs to be taken rather than allowing your feelings to override your good sense.

Like most anxiety-sufferers, you have probably developed the habit of focusing attention on your anxiety whenever it is present, and consequently, may find it difficult to change that habit at first. It often helps to have a few well-rehearsed sayings in your mind, ready to be used when needed. In future, instead of thinking 'What if . . .?', say to yourself 'So what . . .?' Among your repertoire can be sayings like: 'So I'm anxious. It really doesn't matter.' There was one woman who developed a way of treating her anxiety as if it were another person—an unwanted, nuisance of a companion. She would speak to her anxiety and say: 'OK. Since you're here today, I guess you can come with me, but no matter what stunt you pull to try to stop me going to town this morning, I'm going anyway. You can come if you like or you can stay home. It doesn't matter to me, but I'm going.'

A real problem area for women is associated with all of those everyday tasks that have to be done but that require very little concentration or creativity. When an anxiety-sufferer is washing dishes, vacuuming, mowing the lawn, and so on, she often uses that time to focus attention on her anxiety, and this must stop.

When you are washing dishes, try to develop a way of focusing all of your attention on the dishes—how they feel, what they look like, how you are washing them, etc. Whatever task you are doing, put your whole self into the action so that you prevent yourself from becoming preoccupied with your feelings.

Focusing on actions rather than feelings means you become less self-preoccupied, and your anxiety eventually disappears. Anxiety-reduction occurs, then, as a 'by-product of attitudinal acceptance of anxiety and practical action taking' (Ishiyama 1986a, p. 380). In other words, if your attention is deliberately focused on reducing your anxiety, it will not work, but if you change your attitude so that you allow your anxiety to be there while you engage in the practical tasks of everyday living, anxiety-reduction will occur as a by-product of that process.

During Morita therapy, an anxiety-sufferer is asked to begin writing a daily diary, but not the usual kind of diary or journal where one writes about and analyses one's feelings. A strict requirement here is that the diary be a record of activities attempted and accomplished every day, and that no mention be made at all of anxiety feelings. Part of the therapist's role is to read the diary whenever the anxiety-sufferer comes for a therapy session, to ensure that the client is not deviating from the requirement of focusing on actions rather than feelings.

### Focus on physical sensations

To develop the ability to focus your attention deliberately and totally on the task at hand regardless of your anxiety-level is crucial. However, there are times when there is no task to be done—for example, when you go to bed at night—and it is then that a slightly different technique is required.

If anxiety or panic comes upon you at the end of the day when everything is quiet and you are trying to relax and go to sleep, the first thing to do is acknowledge and accept your anxiety feelings. Say, 'It's all right. I'm just going to lie here and let it come if it wants to. I know it can't hurt me and it will pass.' This technique is called *flooding*. Allow the feelings to flood over you while you try to relax and accept what is happening. If you find relaxation exercises helpful (some anxiety-sufferers do not find them helpful), make a deliberate attempt to relax your body as you lie there. The kind of relaxation exercise that makes you focus on the muscles in each part of your body in turn is usually the best, because it takes your focus off your feelings and on to your body. It is not the relaxation that is important so much as the deliberate focusing away from your feelings. If the anxiety persists, of course, it is better not to continue lying there becoming more and more distressed and anxious. Under these circumstances, you must get up and do something till it passes.

The technique of flooding can be used in any situation. As will be seen in the case study to follow, instead of focusing on practical action, an anxiety-sufferer may choose to deal with her anxiety by actually stopping the task she is involved in, sitting in a comfortable chair and allowing the anxiety to flood in on her. The focus of her attention, however, is to be on her physical sensations rather than her emotions. If you choose this technique, you will sit there, maybe with your eyes closed (whatever feels comfortable to you), focusing attention on your body and saying out loud something like this: 'I am aware that my arms are resting on the arms of the chair. My feet are flat on the floor. I observe a tightness in my throat. I observe that my body wants to get up and pace about, but I've decided just to continue sitting here. I observe an ache in my shoulders and neck . . .'

Focusing on bodily sensations while allowing the anxiety to be there will result in the anxiety eventually subsiding. Following such an experience, you may feel somewhat exhausted but you will also feel that you have taken a huge step toward overcoming your anxiety. You have allowed your anxiety to do its worst and you still survived!

## 6 Get on with your life

When you no longer feel compelled to focus all your attention on your anxiety, to hold yourself back from productive and constructive living because of your constant preoccupation with anxiety, you are free to get on with your life. This is the final step in the Morita treatment process.

## Case story of success using Morita therapy

The following is an illustration of successful treatment after a single session of therapy, copied in full from an article by Dr F. Ishu Ishiyama, and while cure does not always occur so quickly, it is helpful to see how this particular therapy session proceeded and the immediate effect it had on someone who was totally committed to the treatment process.

Mary was 35 years old, healthy, physically fit, married but dissatisfied, and working as an administrator at a community-based mental health service. She appeared to be verbal and articulate, intelligent, and self-confident. She visited the author as therapist with a complaint of the fear of death and going insane with an incapacitating anxiety attack (shallow breathing, heart palpitations, and an obsessive fear of death), which she had suffered since childhood. According to her a typical anxiety attack would usually last from a half hour to several hours followed by physical and mental exhaustion.

Mary could not think of any traumatic incidents or rational explanations for the fear. Usually the onset of an anxiety attack had been very sudden and uncorrelated with external events. Concerned about heart problems, she had visited a physician who found no organic malfunction. Her fear of death had become more intense after her husband's minor heart problem two years earlier. Mary had provided the therapist with a brief written description of her problem as requested by him prior to the first session.

After briefly going over the factual information provided by Mary, the therapist asked her to recall a typical experience of her anxiety. As she recalled a recent minor anxiety attack, three basic self-statements were identified: i) I'm going to die for sure this time; ii) How inadequate I am! I can't even control or stop my reactions; iii) I haven't accomplished much in my life and I'm going to die. These generated feelings of panic, self-directed anger and shame, and sadness and regret, respectively.

The therapist drew her attention to her irrational belief that shallow breathing and heart-pounding should lead to eventual death. Mary was aware of its irrationality, but she said that the fear of death and mental disintegration was so intense and felt so real that she had never succeeded in talking herself out of it. The therapist empathically reflected on how scared she was of dying of a heart attack, going insane, and losing control over herself. He also pointed out how she had selectively focused her attention on subtle physiological changes, regarding them as abnormal and anticipating that they would get worse and worse. He reflected that the more she had noticed such anxiety symptoms the worse they had become.

The therapist explained to Mary how anticipation could sensitize a person to even the slightest signs of what is feared, and how exclusive focusing on such anxiety symptoms could escalate a normal and acceptable physiological response into a full-blown panic. He pointed out how counterproductive her attempts to manipulate anxiety had been and how her catastrophic expectation of uncontrolled anxiety had aggravated anxiety symptoms.

The therapist then offered the client a new interpretation of anxiety—a reflection of one's desire to live in good health and in rewarding relationships with others. He pointed out how she had been ignoring this desire for constructive living while overfeeding her fear of death.

First puzzled and then delighted, Mary animatedly responded to this interpretation by saying: 'You mean my anxiety is nothing I should be ashamed of? Is this how strongly I want to live and how strongly I don't want to die yet? True! I do want to live and do so many things to make my life meaningful. I guess I've been wasting my energy by fighting anxiety instead of redirecting it to something more constructive.'

As homework, the client was asked to follow a set of behavioral instructions in facing the next anxiety attack: i) not to run away from the fear of death, but to sit through the entire anxiety experience; ii) not to do anything to change or eliminate anxiety reactions no matter how uncomfortable they may get; iii) to objectify the experience by observing what happens to the body in detail, and to acknowledge each bodily reaction by saying, 'Okay, I see this and that happening to me, and now such and such are happening'; iv) to try to answer the following questions: Let me see how strong my desire for life is. What actions will make my life more meaningful? Even though I can't control my anxiety, I can choose my action. Then, what should I do to improve the quality of my life in here and now? Mary took note of these specific behavioral instructions, and she was asked to memorize them (Ishiyama 1986b, p. 561).

When Mary went to see her therapist the following week, she reported that she had followed the instructions carefully and had found immediate relief from her anxiety. She said she felt so good that she would not require any further therapy. The therapist asked if she would put her experience in writing and send it to him, which she did gladly. The following is an excerpt:

> I said to myself: 'The strength of this fear indicates the strength of my desire for life.' Then, the usual panic did not last longer than a few minutes although I beckoned to it. I just went along with the experience. Nothing disastrous happened and I was surprised at this. I then started crying thinking how stressful my life-style was. I started thinking of many things I had to work on . . . (Ishiyama 1986b, p. 561).

This client was followed up by the therapist after six months, twelve months, eighteen months, and 40 months, and each time she reported that she was doing very well. She said she felt very competent in dealing with anxiety symptoms whenever they appeared. 'I just take notice of anxious sensations and acknowledge them', she said. 'They then dissipate eventually, while I stay on track without losing sight of my purpose in life' (Ishiyama 1986b, p. 562).

# ADDITIONAL STEPS IN THE THERAPY PROCESS

The above six steps are all that is required to have your anxiety disappear and give you back a feeling of control over your life. Following these steps will allow you to move forward into the future confident that if your anxiety does return, as well it might from time to time, it will never again overwhelm you, because you now know how to deal with it quickly and effectively.

In order to make the therapeutic process complete, however, there are four more steps you are strongly urged to consider. These involve more in-depth psychotherapy than was required in the first part of the treatment. Some anxiety-sufferers prefer not to go on any further for fear of opening up truths about their earlier years that they would rather not face, and pain that they would rather not deal with. Even the thought of it causes them to feel anxious again, and their biggest fear is that such a journey into their past could undo all the good work they have done in the first six steps.

It must be emphasised here that you must not force yourself or allow anyone else to pressure you to delve into the depths of your past if you really prefer to leave it be. If you do decide to, it must be your own choice, and you must do it only when you are ready. My experience as a therapist is that anxiety-sufferers vary in their attitudes to these additional steps. Some want to delve into their past from the very first session of therapy. They are so tired of their anxiety that they are determined to deal with both the symptoms and the causes right from the start. This presents the therapist with a fairly difficult task at first. On the one hand, she must get the anxiety-sufferer to take her attention *off* her feelings in order to relieve the anxiety, and on the other hand, she must get the anxiety-sufferer to focus *on* the feelings of her past and confront them head-on—in order to uncover and come to terms with her own personal experiences of powerlessness, invisibility and emotional trauma that are at the root of her present anxiety condition. To do both at the same time is impossible, so the easiest way for a therapist to proceed is to explain the situation to her client and suggest spending the first two sessions focusing on the immediate problem of how to relieve the anxiety, and then move on to the more in-depth work after that.

Other anxiety-sufferers come to therapy at first for the sole purpose of getting rid of their anxiety, but when they begin to feel better they then become interested in discovering how they came to be that way. They ask the therapist to help them uncover some of the mysteries of their past, so that they can experience themselves in their wholeness. This second part of the therapy can be entered into immediately, or the client may choose to come back to it some months, or even years, later.

Others decide very definitely that all they want out of therapy is to get rid of their anxiety. They have no desire at all to delve into the past.

Whatever decision an anxiety-sufferer makes about her own therapy is her own business, and the therapist must be guided at all times by the client's wishes. It is imperative that therapists remain sensitive to the fact that 'psychotherapy is likely to create anxiety . . . [and] be careful that the arousal of anxiety does not become too great . . .' (Meares 1980, p. 56). If an anxiety-sufferer wishes to proceed, the following steps will ensure the most effective therapeutic result.

## 7 Develop a stronger sense of self

Here you begin to ask in earnest: Who am I? If you use this as an opportunity to focus on your anxiety and ask: What makes me anxious? you will do yourself a great disservice. A better understanding of the cause of your anxiety may come as a result of your self-exploration, but the aim here is to develop a much more comprehensive understanding of who you are and in so doing, strengthen your sense of self. This is best done with the help of a skilled psychotherapist, and the process consists of two parts.

First, with the therapist's help, you begin to open up your past. Pull it apart, so to speak, in order to take an honest look at your past in all its different aspects. Recall incidents and relationships, and as you talk, you will find that more and more incidents will come to mind, and more and more feelings will well up inside you. Most of the feelings will make you uncomfortable at first because they will be feelings you repressed, feelings from which you have protected yourself till now. It is important that you allow the feelings to come, and in fact that you immerse yourself in them. Whatever has been buried deep inside you—pain, loneliness, confusion, humiliation, fear, anger—must be recognised and expressed in order for you to be released from its control, and a competent therapist can help you do that.

One of the reasons why many anxiety-sufferers find it difficult to confront the pain of the past is that it often means admitting that their parents were less than perfect, and allowing themselves to feel anger toward one or both parents. To express anger about parents can be frightening and the subsequent guilt can be overwhelming, but it must be done if one is to relate to one's past honestly.

Having pulled your past apart, identified experiences of powerlessness, invisibility and emotional deprivation, and expressed feelings of sadness, grief, anger and so on, the second part of the process is to put it all back together again. The therapeutic value of expressing feelings that have long been unexpressed lies, on the one hand, in being able to release a lifetime of emotions that have been stored up inside you and, on the other hand, in giving you the opportunity to relate to your past in a new way. Prior to therapy, you related to your past as something almost separate from yourself, vague, confusing and overpowering, whereas after therapy, with a new awareness of your past, you are able to incorporate it into your present understanding of who you are, and experience yourself as a whole and integrated person, totally in charge of your own life.

In addition to the above—a better understanding of yourself, the experience of yourself as a whole and integrated person, and the ability to be totally in charge of your own life—the results of 'reworking' the past through in-depth psychotherapy also include: a much stronger self-esteem; the development of a much more powerful 'self-affirmation'; the ability to establish a relationship with your parents (either in your mind or in reality) that is more real, and therefore more satisfying because it is based on a more honest interpretation of the past; and also the ability generally to have more satisfying relationships at every level both now and in the future.

## 8  Allow yourself to feel and express anger

Anger has been called 'the misunderstood emotion' (Tavris 1982), because most people see the expression of anger as unacceptable. Children, especially girls, are punished for outbursts of anger, and they learn very early to keep their angry feelings to themselves. By the time those children become adults most of them are adept at hiding their anger. Some are so good at it that they even hide it from themselves, so that when they somewhat self-righteously say: 'I never get angry', they really believe that to be true.

The truth about anger is that it is a normal, healthy emotion, and that everybody gets angry sometimes. Some, however, have become so practised at ignoring their angry feelings that they literally do not know they are angry. This is particularly unhealthy because anger that is not expressed does not disappear. Rather, it stays inside a person and festers and can cause any number of physiological and psychological problems, such as hypertension, ulcers, headaches, depression, alcoholism, overeating, anxiety and so on (Rubin 1969).

Repressed anger from the past must be released, usually with the help of a therapist, and anger that occurs on a day-to-day basis in the present must be recognised, experienced and expressed.

The reason why many people prefer not to express their anger is because they see its expression always as destructive. They think it always has to mean exploding, yelling, screaming, putting someone else down and so on, but it does not have to be like that. As a matter of fact, it is better and usually more effective to express anger in words, to say in an assertive manner exactly what you think and how you feel. The day-to-day expression of anger prevents it building up and causing problems, and for people prone to anxiety-related conditions, such spontaneous expression of anger is imperative.

Some anxiety-sufferers attest to the fact that when they started expressing their anger, they began to feel more in control of their lives. One woman said: 'I always felt anxious standing in line at the supermarket, but one day I was angry at having to wait so long knowing that Daniel was waiting for me to pick him up at school. Later, when I thought about it, I realised that while I was angry, I forgot about my anxiety, and I felt stronger.' Another anxiety-sufferer tells about what happened when she began to allow herself to feel angry. She became angry at everything and everyone, without really understanding why. 'It just seemed to flow out of me', she said. 'Normally I would have felt guilty, but this time, I felt good—and to my surprise, my anxiety began to be less of a problem.'

## 9  Learn to be more assertive

Although anxiety-sufferers are often pleasant people who smile a lot and try to please, this does not mean they are strangers to assertiveness. Like most people, they are more assertive in some areas of their lives than others, and it is usually true that their anxiety is closely connected with those areas in which they are less assertive.

To learn the skill of assertiveness and be able to use that skill in every sphere of life is important to an anxiety-sufferer because assertiveness means personal empowerment, and empowerment brings a feeling of control.

## 10  Take conscious control of your own life

When you deliberately and consciously move towards developing a stronger sense of self, when you begin to express your anger and other feelings more spontaneously, and when you put into practice the skill of assertiveness day-by-day, you are well on the way to feeling totally in control of your life.

The call to take conscious control of your own life is, in fact, a call to be authentic. The person who is living a life that is controlled by others can be said to be inauthentic because it is not she who is living her life. Others are living it for her and she is just following after them, doing what she perceives they want her to do. To be authentic, that is, to live a life that is real, one must take charge of one's own life.

Women find this particularly difficult because it goes against all of society's expectations of them. Women are expected to be the ones who follow after, the ones who wait, and the ones who 'fit in', so that men can do whatever they want to do, assured of the patient support of the women in their lives. And so that society, made by men for men, can continue to function as it always has with a minimum of disruption. When a woman decides to take control of her own life, there is much resistance from those who usually benefit from her passivity. As you begin to live your life as the one fully in charge, it will not be easy at first because you will meet with resistance, but it is important not to give in. Husbands/partners and children are inclined not to take women seriously, but if you persist in your determination to be in charge of your life, they often come to realise that the happiest and healthiest relationships are those between independent, individual people who are all exercising right of control over their own lives and being careful to respect each other's rights at the same time.

## If you seek the help of a therapist

This book is written with self-help in mind. Anxiety-sufferers who read this book and commit themselves to the first six steps of the treatment process set out above ought to experience relief from their anxiety without the need to see a therapist. However, if you prefer to work through the treatment with the aid of a therapist, that also will be helpful provided you heed the following warning.

In the distant and not-so-distant past, there have been serious deficiencies in the treatment of severe anxiety which have caused additional problems for anxiety-sufferers. In most cases, wrong or deficient treatment results in the prolonging and intensifying of anxiety, together with heightened feelings of hopelessness and helplessness. There has been, and continues to be, a lack of understanding of the condition by some therapists, doctors and psychiatrists, and consequently, if you decide to seek help to get on top of your anxiety, you must choose your therapist carefully. The following advice is important.

### Avoid long-term drug therapy

This is the treatment method favoured by doctors and psychiatrists who value drug therapy over every other kind of therapy, but the fact is that the use of drugs alone has no effect at all on a person's total anxiety condition. A drug may allow a person to function better and feel less anxious while she is taking it, but as soon as the drug is withdrawn, the anxiety is experienced as severely as ever.

There are times when anti-anxiety drugs can be useful on a short-term basis, namely, when a person has become so agitated by her anxiety as to be unable to settle herself to reading a book like this or unable to concentrate long enough to talk with a therapist to gain some understanding of what is happening to her. In these situations, mild anti-anxiety medication can be used for a brief period (say, ten to fourteen days) to allow the therapy process to begin. When choosing a therapist, it is suggested that anxiety-sufferers avoid doctors or psychiatrists who are known to use long-term drug therapy for anxiety-related conditions.

### Avoid shock therapy

Many anxiety-sufferers in the past have been subjected to shock therapy (ECT), and even though there is no real evidence of its effectiveness it continues to be the preferred method of a few psychiatrists today. Anxiety-sufferers should be aware that this is the most seriously deficient and potentially harmful method of treatment available, and it should be avoided at all costs.

### Avoid in-depth psychotherapy until you feel ready for it

As mentioned before, it is a mistake for an anxiety-sufferer to allow herself to be pressured into the kind of therapy where she has to delve into the pain of her past. In-depth psychotherapy can cause anxiety to increase, and while it is helpful if the timing is right, it must be entered into only when the person herself is ready. Therapists who see this kind of psychotherapy as the only way to treat anxiety should be avoided.

### Avoid relaxation therapy as an end in itself

Relaxation therapy can be an important part of an anxiety-sufferer's treatment, but the emphasis is on the word 'part'. A therapist whose response to a person presenting with anxiety

problems is simply to start her on a program of relaxation therapy, is confusing anxiety with stress. While severe anxiety is
certainly stressful, it is a mistake to treat it simply as a result of
stress. It is suggested that therapists whose only course of treatment is positive thinking and relaxation therapy not be avoided
totally, but be seen as offering short-term relief rather than cure.

### Avoid self-help groups that encourage you to focus on your anxiety

While self-help groups in many areas are found to be extremely
valuable to the participants, such groups for agoraphobics and
other anxiety-sufferers are usually a mistake. If anxiety-sufferers
came together in a self-help group every week to talk about
what they had done during the week, that is, to focus on actions
rather than feelings, it would probably be a helpful experience,
but usually participants are encouraged to talk about their
anxiety, and (as Morita treatment shows) such preoccupation
with anxiety only aggravates it and makes it worse.

So-called self-help groups that encourage anxiety-sufferers to
focus on their anxiety and share their experiences of anxiety
should be avoided.

## Roles of anxiety-sufferer, therapist and support-person

It will be helpful to conclude by summarising the roles of the
three people who are usually the key figures in any anxiety-
sufferer's journey towards a cure.

### The role of the anxiety-sufferer

As an anxiety-sufferer intent on a cure, it is imperative that you:

- be committed to the treatment process, and believe that
  it will work;
- accept your anxiety and let it be;
- learn about your anxiety;
- deliberately reinterpret your anxiety;
- do not indulge in anxious preoccupation with your
  symptoms;

- focus your attention on productive tasks rather than feelings;
- concentrate on living a normal life;
- develop a stronger sense of self;
- delve into the pain and fears of your past only if and when you feel ready;
- allow yourself to feel and express anger;
- learn to be more assertive;
- take conscious control of your own life.

### The role of the therapist

As a therapist intent on being as effective as possible, it is important that you:

- allow/encourage the anxiety-sufferer to talk and express feelings;
- be empathic;
- be confident in your own ability to help;
- do not do anything to encourage self-preoccupation;
- learn as much as you can about the condition;
- become familiar with the Morita method of treatment, and the philosophy behind it;
- incorporate the role of 'teacher' into your image of yourself as therapist, and teach anxiety-sufferers about the condition and how to deal with it;
- be careful not to push the anxiety-sufferer in a way that would create more anxiety;
- continue to be supportive.

### The role of the support-person

As a support-person intent on being as helpful as possible, it is important that you:

- be empathic and supportive;
- learn about the condition;
- try to understand that it is a devastating and debilitating condition, and do not be tempted to trivialise it;

- do not put your need to help and your feelings of helplessness on to the anxiety-sufferer. It is not her responsibility to make you feel better;
- do not try to find a reason for every anxiety attack, because there is no reason;
- do not encourage self-preoccupation;
- be careful not to push the anxiety-sufferer to get involved in productive action. It has to be her decision and her timing;
- trust her to deal with her anxiety at her own pace;
- be sensitive to her feelings, and support her without smothering her.

## Conclusion

By faithfully following the first six steps outlined in this final chapter, you *will* overcome your anxiety and once again experience control over your own life. Then, if you decide to delve into the question of what caused your anxiety condition in the first place, you will gain even more strength as you allow yourself to view the situation of women in society with new eyes. You will see that this present time in history is, indeed, an age of anxiety for women, and that powerlessness, invisibility and emotional deprivation are constant, everyday experiences all women are expected to endure. As you gain more and more courage to open your mind to the real situation of women, and realise that such injustices against women are actually built into the system of a society that operates predominantly for the benefit of men, you will become angry, and will begin to insist on changes both in your own relationships and in the society that condones and perpetuates such injustices.

Where once you were inclined to want to keep the peace and suppress your own opinions, to your detriment, now as a woman with a new awareness of how things are, you have a healthy anger and the energy to push for change, determined to work towards the development of a society that places a high value on equality, fairness and justice for all.

# Further reading

Adler, A. (1928) *Understanding Human Nature* London: George Allen & Unwin

Brownmiller, S. (1975) *Against our Will: Men, Women and Rape* New York: Bantam

Cline, S. and Spender, D. (1987) *Reflecting Men at Twice their Natural Size* London: Fontana

Coote, A. and Campbell, B. (1982) *Sweet Freedom. The Struggle for Women's Liberation* London: Pan Books

de Beauvoir, S. (1952) *The Second Sex* New York: Bantam

Eichenbaum, L. and Orbach, S. (1983) *Understanding Women* Harmondsworth, Middlesex: Penguin

Evans, L. (n.d.) 'Agoraphobia: Answers to a few Questions', unpublished paper

Fodor, I.G. (1974) 'The Phobic Syndrome in Women: Implications for Treatment' in V. Franks and V. Burtle (eds) *Women in Therapy: New Psychotherapies for a Changing Society* New York: Brunner/Mazel

Forward, S. (1987) *Men who hate women and the women who love them* New York: Bantam

Freire, P. (1972) *Pedagogy of the Oppressed* Harmondsworth, Middlesex: Penguin

French, M. (1985) *Beyond Power: On Women, Men and Morals* London: Abacus

Freud, S. (1936) *The Problem of Anxiety* New York: Norton

——(1964) *New Introductory Lectures on Psychoanalysis* Harmondsworth, Middlesex: Penguin

Friedan, B. (1963) *The Feminine Mystique* New York: Penguin

Heath, I.W. (1985) *Incest: A Crime Against Children* Melbourne: Victorian Government Printer

Hite, S. (1987) *Women and Love. A Cultural Revolution in Progress* London: Penguin

Horney, K. (1937) *The Neurotic Personality of our Time* London: Kegan Paul, Trench, Trubner & Co.

——(1939) *New Ways in Psychoanalysis* New York: Norton

Ishiyama, F.I. (1986a) 'Morita Therapy: Its basic features and Cognitive Intervention for Anxiety Treatment' *Psychotherapy* 23, 3, pp. 375–81

——(1986b) 'Positive Reinterpretation of Fear of Death: A Japanese (Morita) Psychotherapy Approach to Anxiety Treatment' *Psychotherapy* 23, 4, pp. 556–62

Kierkegaard, S. (1944) *The Concept of Dread* London: Oxford University Press

May, R. (1950) *The Meaning of Anxiety* New York: Norton

Meares, A. (1967) *Relief Without Drugs* Glasgow: Fontana

Meares, R. (1980) 'A Psychodynamic View of Anxiety' in G.D. Burrows and B. Davies (eds) *Handbook of Studies on Anxiety* Elsevier: North-Holland Biomedical Press

Moore, C.D. (1978) *Science Reports. Understanding Neurotic Disorder* Washington D.C.: US Department of Health, Education and Welfare

Prendergast, F.G. (1968) 'The Treatment of Early Anxiety Neurosis' *The Medical Journal of Australia*, 2, 14, pp. 598–600

Queensland Health Department, Division of Health Promotion booklet (n.d.) 'Stress Management: Strategies for Survival'

Regier, D.A., Boyd, J.H., Burke Jr, J.D., Rae, D.S., Myers, J.K., Kramer, M., Robins, L.N., George, L.K., Karno, M., and Myers, J.K. (1988) 'One-Month Prevalence of Mental Disorders in the United States' *Archives of General Psychiatry* 45, 11, pp. 977–86.

Reynolds, D.K. (1976) *Morita Psychotherapy* Berkeley: University of California Press

——(1984) *Playing Ball on Running Water. The Japanese Way to Building a Better Life* New York: Quill

Rohrbaugh, J.B. (1979) *Women: Psychology's Puzzle* London: Abacus

Rubin, T.I. (1969) *The Angry Book* New York: Collier

Spender, D. (1980) *Man Made Language* London: Routledge & Kegan Paul

Stone, M. (1976) *The Paradise Papers. The Suppression of Women's Rites* London: Virago

Summers, A. (1975) *Damned Whores and God's Police. The Colonization of Women in Australia* Victoria: Penguin

Tavris, C. (1982) *Anger. The Misunderstood Emotion* New York: Simon and Schuster

Tillich, P. (1952) *The Courage to Be* New Haven, Connecticut: Yale University Press

Weekes, C. (1962) *Self Help for your Nerves* London: Angus & Robertson

# INDEX